TELEMENTAL HEALTH with KIDS
Toolbox

102 Games, Play and Art Activities, Sensory and Movement Exercises, and Talk Therapy Interventions

Amy Marschall, PsyD

Published by
PESI Publishing
3839 White Ave
Eau Claire, WI 54703

Cover: Amy Rubenzer
Editing: Jenessa Jackson, PhD
Layout: Baker & Taylor and Amy Rubenzer

9781683734383 (print)
9781683734390 (epub)
9781683734406 (epdf)

Printed in the United States of America.

PESI Publishing
pesipublishing.com

Dedication

This book is dedicated to all of my clients, especially those who underwent the transition from in-person therapy to telehealth in March of 2020.

About the Author

Dr. Amy Marschall is a clinical psychologist who has been providing telemental health services since 2017. She is certified in Telehealth and Trauma-Focused Cognitive Behavioral Therapy, and she has been developing and distributing kid-friendly telehealth resources since April of 2020. When she is not practicing psychology, she is making art and spending time with her husband and two cats.

Table of Contents

Part

1 **An Overview of Telemental Health with Kids** 1

Introduction 1
How to Use This Book 2
Think Outside the Toolbox 2

Telemental Health and Kids: Building Your Confidence 2

Setting the Stage for Telehealth 3
Your Space 4
The Client's Space 5
Talking to Caregivers 6
Helping Kids Engage 7

Part

2 **A Toolbox of Telemental Health Activities** 9

Therapy Games for Telehealth 10
Battleship 11
Checkers 13
Chess 14
Connect Four 16
Crazy Eights 17
Dominoes 18
Duo Survival 19
Foosball 21
Go Fish 22
Grabble 24
Guess Who 25
Hexxagon 26
Jigsaw Puzzles 27
Ludo 28
Mancala 29

Match Up 30

Pictionary 31

Scattergories 33

Snakes and Ladders 34

Tic Tac Toe 35

Trivia 36

Tumbling Tower 37

Uno 38

Yahtzee 40

Art Activities for Telehealth **41**

Auto Draw 42

Camping Trip Drawing: Joint Drawing Task 43

Draw a Garden: Joint Drawing Task 44

Draw Your Family 45

Draw Your Feelings 46

Draw Your Home 48

Etch A Sketch 49

Fear Drawing 50

Mandala Drawing 51

Origami/Paper Folding 52

Safe Place Drawing 53

Sand Drawing 54

Sand Painting 55

Sandscapes 56

Self-Portrait Drawing 57

Weave Silk 58

What If You Were a _____? 59

Body Movement Activities **60**

Body Stretches 61

Charades 62

Dance Party 63

I Can Make My Heart Go Fast 65

Mirroring 66

Muscle Relaxation 67

Scavenger Hunt 68

Shake Out the Wiggles 69

Simon Says 70

Wake Up Your Face Muscles! 71

Sensory Activities **73**

Antistress Game 74

Fidgets 75

Fireworks 76

Mindful Hearing. 77

Mindful Seeing. 79

Mindful Smelling 81

Mindful Tasting 83

Mindful Touch 84

Perception: What Color Do You See?. 85

Rubik's Cube. 86

Sand Tray: Free Play 87

Slime 89

Zen Rock Garden 91

Zen Photon Garden 92

Talking Activities **93**

Alphabet Game. 94

Auto Complete Game 96

Chats 97

Deck of Cards. 98

Meet Your Pets 101

Sentence Stories 102

Three Songs 103

Twenty Questions 104

Virtual Vacations. 106

Vision Boards 107

Would You Rather. 108

Your Story. 110

Tele-Play Therapy **112**

Cars 113

Dollhouse. 114

Escape Rooms. 116

Hatchimals 117

Hide-and-Seek 118

LEGO® 119

Mazes 120

Minecraft 121

Physical Play 122

Puppet Show. 123

Roblox: Adopt Me 124

Roblox: Hide-and-Seek 125

Roblox: Meep City 126

Tag 127

Virtual Backgrounds 128

Cognitive Behavioral Therapy and Telehealth 130

Feelings Thermometer. 131

Big Breath Activities 132

Coping Skills Toolbox. 134

Reaction Videos and Emotion Identification 135

Receiving Help 136

Safety Planning. 137

Safety Plan 138

Thought Record 139

Thought-Stopping Activity: Skip the Song 140

Tornado Brain. 141

How To Create Your Own Telehealth Activities 142

Finding Activities 143

Creating Your Own Activities 143

Playing to Your (Telehealth) Strengths. 144

You've Got This! 145

References 147

Acknowledgments

I want to thank the wonderful people at PESI for the opportunity to share all I've learned about telehealth and kids, both in the form of continuing education seminars and this book. Special thanks to Kate Sample, my contact at PESI Publishing, for the words of support and encouragement while I put this together.

Thank you also to my husband, Mike, for being the best man I've ever met (sorry, everyone else).

Thank you to my cats, Armani and Vera, for helping my clients transition to telehealth and keeping them interested in their sessions while I was figuring out what I was doing.

Thank you to my therapist family, both those I know in person and those I've met online over the past year. I don't know what I would have done as a mental health provider in a pandemic without the support and love from my people.

Part 1

An Overview of Telemental Health with Kids

INTRODUCTION

Don't talk to strangers on the internet! That's what our parents told us, and what we have passed on to our children. But when kids check in to their first telehealth session, this is exactly what we are asking them to do.

Your training probably didn't include how to implement kid-friendly therapeutic techniques in a telehealth setting. If you've found yourself scrambling, feeling overwhelmed, or questioning your ability to do telehealth with kids, this book is for you. If you want to be able to do telehealth with kids effectively, using interventions that fit with their treatment plans and that provide evidence-based outcomes, this is the book for you.

Although some therapists have been using technology to conduct remote sessions with kids for years, the vast majority of therapists have been encouraged to see children in person whenever feasible due to limited evidence on the effectiveness of telehealth with this population. It is a catch-22 we run into in clinical practice: We want to offer competent, evidence-based, effective treatment, but how do we develop such treatments? We have to actually *do* telehealth with kids in order to become competent doing telehealth with kids.

The COVID-19 pandemic created innovation from necessity. Telemental health was widely adopted in response to the pandemic, which allowed us to quite literally meet our clients where they were. And in the long term, telemental health will continue to be beneficial for people living in rural areas, those with mobility or transportation issues, the immunocompromised, families with childcare concerns, and so many others. It was needed long before, and it is definitely here to stay. More and more states are requiring that telehealth services be covered by insurance, and many clients who previously came in person are requesting ongoing telehealth services even after the option of in-person sessions has resumed.

The goal of this book is twofold. I want to provide you with a toolbox packed full of effective interventions that you can use in your telehealth sessions with children, and I want to help you understand that you can offer this service competently. As you will learn, you absolutely *can* offer telehealth with children, and you can do so ethically, confidently, and competently. You can pull from this toolbox whenever you need to, and you can create even more interventions specifically tailored to your own practice. You've got this—and you've got this book to help you!

How to Use This Book

This toolbox is divided into two sections: Part I presents an overview of what telehealth with kids looks like and sets you up to offer this service confidently and effectively, and part II provides 100 ready-made activities to implement in your sessions. These worksheets include suggested age ranges, therapeutic benefits, and specific instructions for use. Part II also includes a chapter on how to develop even more telehealth activities to use in your practice. Use your clinical intuition to determine which activities are the best fit for each client, and remember, you can do this!

Think Outside the Toolbox

As child therapists, we are used to getting creative in our sessions. My aim in writing this book is not only to create a comprehensive toolbox of activities that can benefit a myriad of diagnoses and treatment plans, but also to inspire you to go beyond the interventions presented here and develop an arsenal of kid-friendly telehealth interventions that are unique to your own practice. Being open to feedback from your clients and adjusting your approach as needed will allow you to present each of your clients with opportunities to work through difficulties, process emotions, and develop skills in a way that works for them as an individual.

TELEMENTAL HEALTH AND KIDS: BUILDING YOUR CONFIDENCE

Prior to the COVID-19 pandemic, less than half of providers in the United States offered any telehealth services (Cantor et al., 2021). Most graduate programs cover telehealth only briefly, if at all (in my own program, I recall being told that it was unlikely that I would be doing telehealth more than occasionally). So it makes sense that the adjustment has been a challenge for many providers. Transitioning from in-person sessions to telehealth can be difficult enough with adult clients, even though talk therapy can look very similar online. Sessions with children and teens take even greater adjustment because these groups engage in therapy differently. How can you play hide-and-seek, interact with a dollhouse, or engage in other therapeutic games when you can't share physical space with your clients?

The good news is, although the pool of research around telehealth is growing slowly, the information we have so far shows that telehealth can be effective for children and teens with many different presenting problems—including attention-deficit/hyperactivity disorder (ADHD), eating disorders, anxiety, depression, obsessive-compulsive disorders, trauma, adjustment disorders, and suicidal ideation (Gloff et al., 2015; Moody Fairchild et al., 2020)—and that access to care improves significantly in rural areas when providers are willing to offer telehealth (Moody Fairchild et al., 2020). Despite this, surveys show that therapists' biggest concern surrounding providing telehealth services is that they do not have the ability to do so effectively (Felker et al., 2021).

You have likely asked yourself, "What if I can't do my job at the same level over telehealth? What if I can't adjust? What if I can't be what my clients need?" The fact that you care so much about being effective is a good thing! It's what motivated you to read this book, and it's how I know that you can absolutely do the work to make this adjustment. Studies have shown that clinicians tend to assume that learning telehealth will be much more difficult than it actually is (Felker et al., 2021). In fact, even practitioners who were wary of transitioning to telehealth were able to provide comparable levels of care in a telehealth setting after just six weeks of practice (Sharma et al., 2020).

It sounds simple: The biggest barrier in making the shift to telehealth is convincing yourself that you can do it and overcoming your own insecurities about your skills. But, as therapists, we know this is much easier said than done.

Think back to when you were a student at your first practicum placement. You probably had many of the same thoughts and feelings that you're having right now about telehealth. Maybe you thought that you would never be able to learn the skills to be a good therapist, or maybe you were worried that you would do a bad job and harm your clients. Of course, one thing that helped you overcome these concerns was to just do it. You completed session after session, honed your skills, and became more confident in your style as a therapist. For many, imposter syndrome never completely goes away, but time helps reduce this anxiety around our skills. I hope you feel more competent now than you did when you were going into your first session!

Adjusting to telehealth is similar. Practice makes proficient, and you will get better at this service the longer you offer it. You do have one advantage over your past self: You have the knowledge that you can learn new skills because you've done it before! And while it took you years to learn how to do therapy for the first time, becoming competent in telehealth takes nowhere near that long.

If you are willing to put in the work to learn, you can do telehealth, and you can provide the same level of care that you do in your in-person sessions with kids. Remind yourself as many times as you need to: You can do this!

SETTING THE STAGE FOR TELEHEALTH

It's easy to focus on what you lose when you go from in-person to telehealth sessions with kids, and it's easy to overlook what you gain. Yes, it is more difficult to read body language and assess things like hygiene when you are looking at someone on a screen rather than meeting with them in your office. At the same time, though, meeting with kids in their homes gives you environmental data you just can't learn when they come to your office. For example, many caregivers might describe their homes as "messy," but there is a broad range of what this could mean—telehealth in the client's home shows you exactly what this means for this family.

Most kids are excited to show you around their living space when they first start telehealth sessions, and they might offer you the grand tour without even being asked.

Of course, with telehealth, you are setting up a session that will be conducted in two separate locations rather than one, and you have limited control over one of those locations. In my office, I have a lot of control over what the space looks like, what distractions are present, and what steps are taken to ensure privacy. In telehealth, I have to set up my home office and then help my client set up their space in their home. What does this look like?

Your Space

Whether you do telehealth from your in-person office or from your home, setting the stage for these sessions is different from in-person sessions. There is not one "right" way to set up your office space for telehealth; you can figure out what fits best with your therapeutic style and the tone you want to set in your sessions. However, there are certain things you need to keep in mind.

First and foremost, client privacy is essential. Your workspace should be quiet, confidential, and free of interruptions or distractions. If you are working from home, it is considered best practice to have a note on your home office door indicating that you are working, as well as a note on the front door to your home requesting that people not knock, ring the bell, and so on. Of course, some visitors will ring the bell anyway, but the note discouraging this minimizes how often it occurs.

Will others be in your home while you work? Do you have a roommate, significant other, or child? It is vital that you communicate to them that they cannot interrupt you during a session. (My wording to my husband was "If the apartment is not on fire, do not come to my office while I am working.") This is important both to prevent interruptions and to comply with confidentiality and HIPAA requirements. If someone other than you overhears a part of a session, that's a breach.

It can be helpful to write up a brief business agreement with any other adults who will be in your home while you conduct telehealth sessions. They basically put in writing that they will not interrupt sessions or attempt to overhear what is said. When I was first certified as a telehealth provider, my instructor shared a story of a colleague who got into a nasty divorce, and the therapist's ex-spouse reported to the licensing board that he had overheard session content. The therapist was sanctioned for not doing enough to ensure confidentiality in the home office.

You do not need anything overly complicated for this. A home business agreement simply needs to include:

1. That others in the home understand that your work includes confidential, protected health information
2. That others in the home will not interrupt you while you are working
3. That others in the home will make reasonable efforts to avoid overhearing or seeing anything containing confidential information about your work
4. That, if others in your home accidentally see or overhear something, they will keep that information confidential
5. An agreement about how you are storing work-related information (paperwork, laptop, etc.), including an agreement that others in your home will not attempt to access this information at any time

Now that we have covered confidentiality, you can start to put together your space in a way that fits your needs and preferences. A telehealth office requires a screen, a camera, a microphone, and speakers, all preferably of high quality. I also recommend a good, comfortable chair and (if you plan to use virtual backgrounds) a green screen.

In telehealth the client sees less of the space that you are in, so you need to be mindful of what they can see when your video is on and how this brings them into the session. Do you want books in your background? Toys to communicate playfulness? A blank background without distractions? If you plan to use virtual backgrounds, a green screen or blank wall works best, though it can look kind of boring when you aren't displaying an image behind you.

Also be mindful of what you *don't* want clients to see: Is a messy room visible behind you? Is something visible that would provide information that you are uncomfortable self-disclosing? Imagine seeing your office from the client's perspective—what impression are you giving with your background? Is that what you want to communicate to your clients?

When you enter the frame, are you making sure you are centered? Do you move around a lot in a way that might be distracting? One benefit of telehealth sessions is that it's easy to use a fidget item out of the client's view, so you can keep your hands busy and help your upper body stay still on camera. If there are any physical items you might need for sessions (puppets, toys, markers, etc.), try to have them in arm's reach so you do not have to get up frequently during the session.

This might go without saying, but make sure you are dressed appropriately for your sessions. Yes, comfort is important, and working from home means we are a bit more relaxed in our environment. It can be acceptable to dress down a bit for home sessions, and since clients likely will not see your legs, sweatpants could become work clothes. But don't go without pants or check into sessions in a bathrobe! (In case you're wondering, yes, I did hear secondhand about a client whose therapist joined a telehealth session in a bathrobe.)

Once you have your home office set up the way you want things to look, be aware of your own body's needs while you are working. Those of us who do play therapy are used to moving around quite a bit throughout sessions, and telehealth sessions involve a lot of sitting. Is it easy for you to get in and out of your workspace to stretch in between appointments? Are you going to be comfortable in that seat all day? Would you prefer to use a standing or convertible desk? Do you have water, coffee, or tea within your reach to sip during sessions? A big part of our job is modeling self-care to our clients, which means ensuring that our own needs are met in our telehealth space.

The Client's Space

Although we cannot control what space the client will be in when they check in to their sessions, we have a responsibility to communicate our expectations to the parent or guardian prior to the start of therapy. Each client will have their own "office" from which they join you for sessions, and some clients might check in from different locations depending on the day.

As with your telehealth office, the number-one priority is that your clients have privacy during their sessions. I let the caregivers know that it is their responsibility to ensure that the child has a private space during their sessions and open up a discussion about what this means. Usually, this conversation goes well, and the caregivers take the child's privacy needs seriously from there. Sometimes, though, this must be addressed as an ongoing issue. If you notice your client seems to be looking at or interacting with someone off camera, or you hear voices in the background, you need to pause the session to investigate this. We cannot control if someone else is present in a session, and it is possible for this to occur without our knowledge, but when we have reason to believe that privacy is compromised, we have a duty to look into it.

Once privacy has been established, you can help the caregivers set up a space that will be beneficial to therapy. One advantage of telehealth is that children who are being seen from their homes can have a space that is tailored to their specific preferences and needs. You might have had times in your in-person office when a certain toy or intervention was not appropriate for a specific child, and you had to remember to put it away before they arrived—with telehealth, you do not have to create the child's space because they have created it themselves!

Be open, be flexible, and be creative. Each family's home can present unique challenges to creating a space that is appropriate for telehealth. For example, many kids do not have their own bedroom, but the expectation can be established that the client will have privacy in that space during their sessions. You can work with the caregivers to determine what will be best for their situation.

Generally, I recommend that the child's therapy space have minimal distractions. I allow and encourage the child to bring toys or games that will be used in the session, but I encourage caregivers to keep these items to a minimum so they don't distract the child or prevent them from engaging in their session.

As you communicate expectations about privacy at the onset of treatment, you must also let caregivers know your policy about checking in from different locations. You have some flexibility in deciding what your policy is on this, but certain considerations are important. If a client joins their session from a very public place with other people around, it's typically best to cancel the session due to privacy concerns. If you made this policy known at the onset of treatment, you have the right to count that appointment as a "no-show" and handle it based on your policy about no-shows. The client did not show up to the appointment from a location that permitted the session to continue, after all. However, if the child checks in from a public place but does have privacy—maybe they're in their caregiver's vehicle, which is parked away from other people—you might choose to move forward with the session if you are able.

Since you do not have control over the child's location in a telehealth session, establishing open communication and boundaries about what is needed and what is acceptable is vital.

Talking to Caregivers

One big barrier to buy-in with telehealth is getting caregivers on board. Though telehealth has become more common in recent years, many caregivers are still hesitant about trying this method for receiving therapy services. If you do not offer in-person sessions or these sessions are not feasible based on the client's location, you can suggest that the caregivers try telehealth for their child with the knowledge that they can request a referral for in-person services if it does not work. I have found that most kids take to telehealth very well when given the chance, but when caregivers are unsure, I communicate to them that I am open to changing my approach if it is not effective, which puts them at ease and makes them more willing to try.

It can be helpful to let caregivers know that there is peer-reviewed research showing that telehealth is effective for kids and teens with many different presenting problems, including thoughts of self-harm or suicide (Moody Fairchild et al., 2020), and that telehealth can be effective for children as young as 3 years old (Schoenfelder Gonzalez et al., 2021).

Make sure that the caregivers have a clear understanding of the expectations for therapy, including privacy, what the child should have for sessions, where the caregiver should be during sessions, and how you and the caregiver will check in about the child's therapy.

As with in-person therapy for kids, caregivers are sometimes understandably uncertain about what therapy looks like with their child. I find it helpful to explain to them my therapeutic style, including what this looks like in a telehealth session.

Helping Kids Engage

Although kids have varying levels of comfort with technology, they tend to take well to telehealth when given the proper resources (Archard et al., 2021). Children tend to learn new technology quickly and can adapt to telehealth sessions in most cases.

If a child is having trouble understanding the telehealth system, use this as an opportunity to model maintaining a calm demeanor, and talk them through the challenges. You can show them that they are capable of doing difficult things and that you are there to help them learn something new. Typically, after a few sessions, children get the hang of the technology and are able to engage easily in their sessions.

Though children tend to pick up the tech side of telehealth fairly quickly, they can have a more difficult time keeping themselves in view or directing their words toward the microphone. In my office, if a child moves away from where I am, I can simply follow them. In telehealth, I am stuck wherever they placed the device and end up looking at whatever the camera is facing. It is important for me to be able to see and hear my clients, so when they are out of view or I cannot hear them, I cue them to come back to me.

When redirecting a child, the most important thing is to do so with gentleness and patience—and without reprimanding. It can be frustrating to remind a child for the third time in five minutes that you cannot see them if they run across the room, but the therapy space relies on our ability to stay calm in this moment. I make statements like "Oh no, I can't see you!" or "I couldn't quite hear that—could you please lean closer to the microphone and tell me again?" Rather than scolding the child for failing to stay in the frame, I am communicating that I want to see them and hear what they have to say. I am building our relationship!

Another challenge we face in telehealth sessions is helping kids engage in their sessions. If a child shuts down or does not want to engage in my office, the shared physical space allows me to remain fully present with them as they work through their apprehension. With telehealth, there are a few different options if a child is struggling to engage:

1. You can ask the caregiver to join you in the session and help the child remain focused on the session. This is often helpful with very young children, but you want to make sure that the caregiver understands and is able to provide therapeutic redirection rather than punishment when the child is having trouble.

2. You can shift to a nondirective approach and simply narrate what is happening in the moment rather than trying to introduce a particular intervention. This can help children engage if they are ignoring you and doing another activity, as it shows them that you are present in the session and are able to adjust the plan based on their needs.

3. You can ask the child what they would be doing if they were not in a session right now but still on the device (for example, "What would you be doing if you were on your tablet but I wasn't here?"). Every child has some screen time activity that they enjoy, and inviting them to share that activity with you can build rapport. Besides, I have found that many of these activities can be worked into the child's treatment plan if we are willing to get creative!

4. You can name the awkwardness of the moment. Kids have responded positively to me pointing out that this is different, weird, or not what they were expecting, and this lets them know it is okay to tell me what they are thinking, even if it is something negative.

Moving to an online office is an adjustment with different considerations and steps from in-person sessions, and building rapport can look different online than it did with in-person sessions, but you have the knowledge to make it work and tailor your telehealth sessions to your style, population, and needs. Now that we have established how to set up your office, help your clients put their space together, and engage both children and caregivers in telehealth, we are ready to explore more specific tools and techniques you can use in your practice!

A Toolbox of Telemental Health Activities

Now that you are ready to begin using telehealth with your clients, what do you do in your actual sessions? Just as when you see kids in person in your office, conducting teletherapy with children is an intricate balance of rapport, engagement, and interventions that fit with the child's treatment plan.

This section presents a series of ready-to-use, telehealth-friendly interventions, including the mechanics of setup and the therapeutic benefits of each. You can keep these activities on hand and decide before each session or in the moment which interventions are most appropriate for each client. Each activity has a suggested age range, but of course, you are encouraged to use your clinical judgment to determine what each of your clients needs.

At the end of this toolbox, you will find a how-to guide that will help you create even more telehealth games and activities, as well as transition your favorite in-person interventions to a telehealth setting. With this knowledge, you can continue to expand this toolbox and customize it to your own practice.

Child therapists tend to keep a variety of board games in their offices for use during sessions. Each game has different benefits, but they all tend to help build rapport and lower clients' inhibitions or anxieties about being in the session. All board games have an element of taking turns, which can build social skills, frustration tolerance, and emotion regulation when the client is losing, and sportsmanship when they are winning. This section details how you can play 24 different games with clients over telehealth in a way that has similar therapeutic benefits to your in-person sessions. There are tips included for incorporating more specific therapeutic work into each game, but all the options presented here lend themselves to therapy on their own and can foster rapport. As always, use your clinical judgment to determine what is appropriate in each situation.

Most of the games involve using a website to host the game, and moves are made on the screen. I have found this to be particularly helpful with kids who might wander off during their appointment. Although you and your client will be able to hear each other while playing the game and will probably be able to see each other unless the client is using a smartphone for their session, some kids also like to play around with the built-in chat feature that some of the websites include. It is important to make sure that they understand not to use the chat feature to talk about the session because it is not encrypted. You can use these games and still be HIPAA compliant with your session, as any breach would only allow someone to see that a game is being played, not who is playing or that the game is part of a therapy session. But if your client types something about their mental health in the chat, that is not guaranteed to be private.

Many of the games have rules coded in. This saves time if you are introducing a game that is new to the child, as the website teaches them the rules as they go, and you typically do not have to go over the rules more than once. It does limit your ability to take a nondirective approach, if this is your therapeutic orientation, as the child cannot change the rules, cheat, or give themselves certain advantages that you might usually allow them. On the other hand, though, if a child has treatment goals related to emotion regulation, you can work through the frustration induced while preserving rapport. For example, when a child who wants to take extra turns becomes angry that they are not able to, you can say, "*I* would love to allow you extra turns, but that is not possible in this game—so how can we work through it together?"

I recommend walking through the setup of various games with a colleague, friend, or family member before using them in sessions. The setup itself promotes communication skills, and it goes much smoother if you understand the steps before trying with a client. Play around with the various options within each game and see which ones fit best in your practice.

Battleship

Suggested Age Group: 6 and up

Therapeutic Benefits: Working memory, focus, frustration tolerance, planning

Telehealth Benefits: If you are playing using the website, you make your guesses by pointing and clicking. This allows for uninterrupted conversation while playing the game. The rules are coded into the game, and your client cannot see where you placed your ships, which prevents cheating. Since there is an option for random ship placement, you can get into the game more quickly because you don't spend time deciding where to put each ship. Plus, you won't constantly find those pegs around your office!

Therapy Suggestions:

1. Have the client share a positive feeling when they make a hit and a negative feeling when they miss.

2. When you make a hit, have the client talk about a time when something didn't go their way.

3. Offer "warm" or "cold" clues to help the client find your ships.

Setup: Go to www.en.battleship-game.org. You must choose either "classic" (the standard five ships from the board game) or "Russian" (ten smaller ships). Ships can be placed by clicking and dragging, or you can click "randomize." Copy and paste the link to share with your client. If the client wants to go first, ensure that they click "play" before you do.

Alternate Setup: If both you and your client own the board game Battleship, you can play using the physical game over telehealth! Simply set up the game as you normally would. With this setup, you still have to make your guesses out loud.

Additional Notes: Battleship has been a popular telehealth game. Kids like that they can choose how many ships there will be, and I have been able to process frustration with the game in real time because we do not have to interrupt the conversation to state our guesses. If you are able to use the actual board game, kids who are struggling to adjust to online sessions may prefer the familiarity of physical play with a classic game that they already know.

Sometimes, I will keep my ships in the same place for multiple rounds of play. This leads to the game doubling as a working memory exercise, as kids can gain an advantage if they are able to remember where my ships were during the last round.

Whatever approach you take to this game, Battleship is a great way to engage kids, and the skills used in the game can apply to various treatment goals.

Checkers

Suggested Age Group: 4 and up

Therapeutic Benefits: Focus, frustration tolerance, planning, taking turns, following rules, impulse control

Telehealth Benefits: The rules are coded into the game, so when the client selects which piece they want to move, it shows them what the choices are. This means you do not have to spend time teaching them how to play, and you can work through frustration with having to follow rules we might not like without having to enforce them yourself. This maintains therapeutic rapport while still bringing about the feelings in real time.

Therapy Suggestions:

1. Share a feeling every time you capture an opponent's piece.

2. Share something you are good at every time you get a king.

3. Do stretches (or other body work) when the opponent captures one of your pieces.

Setup: Go to www.247Checkers.com and select "2 player." You get to select whether red or black goes first, and you have the option to force players to jump when they have the opportunity or not. Usually I turn this option off, as it gives me more freedom to "go easy" on kids who are still learning the game. You can also choose whether or not the game shows you what moves a piece can do when you click on it—again, this can be helpful for young kids who are still learning to play. Once you have made your selections, click "play." Share your screen with your client, and grant them remote control. Take turns controlling the screen to make each of your moves.

Additional Notes: Checkers is a great therapy game because the rules are simple and easy to remember, and it is a game that even very young children can understand and learn to play. With this version, you can "show moves" to give the client extra help knowing what their choices are. Since both players are controlling the screen, it becomes important to wait your turn, which takes patience. Though you can add more therapeutic pieces to this game, standard checkers is a great way to build rapport early in the therapy process.

Chess

Suggested Age Group: 6 and up

Therapeutic Benefits: Executive functioning, focus, frustration tolerance, planning, problem solving, impulse control

Telehealth Benefits: The game teaches you the rules as you play, so you do not have to spend time teaching clients the rules. And the rules are coded into the game, so you can balance giving clients a sense of control in their sessions and enforcing boundaries and rules in this game to get the benefits of chess as a therapeutic intervention. You are free to focus on rapport as the game enforces the rules.

Setup: Go to www.lichess.org and select "play with a friend." You can choose to have time limits or select "unlimited" under "time control." Click which color you want to be, or click "random." Copy and paste the link to share with your client.

Variations:

1. *Standard:* Traditional chess with standard rules. I'm sure you are familiar.

2. *Crazy House:* A twist on the traditional game where, after you capture your opponent's piece, you can place it on the board as your own. You have to be mindful of what pieces you sacrifice, since losing your queen means your opponent gets a second one!

3. *Chess960:* Traditional chess, except the starting placement of the pieces is randomized.

4. *King of the Hill:* The goal is to get your king to the center of the board first.

5. *Three-Check:* Similar to standard chess, except the game is over when someone gets in check for the third time regardless of whether it's checkmate.

6. *AntiChess:* Your goal is to run out of pieces. If you can capture your opponent's piece, you must capture it, and you win when you have no pieces left on the board.

7. *Atomic:* Traditional chess, except when you capture a piece, it creates an "explosion" where all adjacent pieces are also taken out.

8. *Horde:* Black has the standard chess pieces. White has 36 pawns. White wins when black is in checkmate; black wins when white runs out of pieces.

9. *Racing Kings:* Both players start on the same side of the board, and you are trying to get your king to the other side first.

10. *From Position:* Standard chess with customized setup. You (or your client) can choose to add or take away pieces. Some clients like to try out different combinations, and some who are still learning like to give themselves an advantage by getting extra pieces or having me start without a queen. The possibilities are endless!

Additional Notes: When I was a graduate student, a supervisor told me that chess is the "ultimate" therapy game, so I have always tried to offer it in my sessions. This was the first game I incorporated over telehealth, and it remains a favorite with my clients. The variations keep them interested and add challenges as they get better at the game, and the skills it builds apply to a huge variety of treatment plans. Using the website, you can implement different versions of the game without having spare pieces on hand, and you can challenge your client with less strain on the therapeutic relationship.

Connect Four

Suggested Age Group: 5 and up

Therapeutic Benefits: Focus, planning, executive functioning, taking turns, social skills

Telehealth Benefits: The online version of Connect Four randomizes what color each person is and who goes first, which means that the child has to practice allowing someone else to go ahead of them. It also switches what color each player is, which can be confusing but means that you have to pay even closer attention. The version I am familiar with is timed, which can be a helpful exposure if the client has anxiety about timed tasks, and if you run out of time in your turn, the game makes a random move for you, which teaches consequences. I really like that the game automatically tells you when someone wins, since many times in my office I've gotten caught up in what the client and I were discussing and not realized that one of us had four in a row!

Setup: Go to https://c4arena.com/ and click "play with friend." You can enter a nickname or leave it blank (in which case you will be listed as "opponent"). Copy the generated link and send it to the client. (Be aware: If you are using Zoom, the link will not be clickable in the chat unless you add "https://" at the beginning.)

Additional Notes: I like Connect Four as a therapy game because it is simple and easy to play, and it teaches some great skills. To win the game, you have to be mindful of both where you are putting your pieces and where your opponent is putting theirs. The telehealth version has the added time limit, which can help with real-time anxiety management and frustration tolerance.

Crazy Eights

Suggested Age Group: 5 and up

Therapeutic Benefits: Taking turns, following rules, reducing anxiety about the session

Telehealth Benefits: No shuffling, and no lost cards! This is a simpler version of Uno, so younger kids might have an easier time with the rules. The platform I recommend for this game is more open than most of the telehealth games in this book, so there is room to let the child make their own rules.

Therapy Suggestions:

1. Give a category to each suit (or each number). For example:

   - *Hearts are feelings.* When you play a heart, name a feeling and share a time you've felt that way.

   - *Clubs are thoughts.* Name a thought you had recently that was not helpful, and share how you know it was not helpful.

   - *Spades are choices.* Name a choice you made recently that had negative consequences.

   - *Diamonds are rewards.* Name a reward you earned recently and how you earned it.

2. Get your body moving with the game! When you play a numbered card, do that number of jumping jacks (or push-ups, sit-ups, etc.) or that many seconds of a body stretch.

Setup: Go to https://playingcards.io/ and scroll down to Crazy Eights. Select "create room," and send the link to your client.

Additional Notes: Simple card games like Crazy Eights can be great at the start of therapy because the act of engaging in the card game takes pressure off of the conversation and puts clients at ease. They can focus on playing the game, and this frees them up to speak more openly about why they are there or what they hope to get out of therapy. The added activities noted under the Therapy Suggestions section can make this game relate more directly to their treatment plan if desired and add a fun layer to the game.

Dominoes

Suggested Age Group: 6 and up

Therapeutic Benefits: Focus, planning, taking turns, frustration tolerance

Telehealth Benefits: Dominoes is a relatively simple game—you place pieces with matching sides and try to be the first one out. There is some strategy to the game, but you also rely on luck. One downside to playing Dominoes over telehealth is that you cannot let the client win by drawing when you actually could play a piece, but this opens up exposure to frustration and real-time practice of emotion regulation. When it is your turn, the game highlights which pieces you can choose from, which is helpful because it teaches the client how to play and gives them suggestions without you seeing their pieces.

Therapy Suggestions:

1. Have each number represent a feeling, and talk about a time you had that feeling when you place a tile with that number. It can be engaging to let the client pick which feeling goes to each number.

2. Share something that happened when you were the age of the number you put down. (This version uses 0 to 6 dots, so this would be an exploration of early childhood memories.)

Setup: Go to https://dominoes.playdrift.com/ and select "new game," "private," then "create room." Send the link to your client and have them join you in the room.

Additional Notes: Kids were generally not interested in playing Dominoes in my office. Some liked to line the Dominoes up and knock them over, but the traditional Dominoes game was not of general interest. Strangely, many kids request it as a telehealth activity. It's simple and easy to explain, and it can be a lot of fun to play.

Duo Survival

Suggested Age Group: 8 and up

Therapeutic Benefits: Problem solving, teamwork, cooperative play, asking for help, frustration tolerance

Telehealth Benefits: Although I have cooperative board games that I used in my office, Duo Survival is not available as an in-person game to my knowledge. I have not been able to find free cooperative board games for use on telehealth, though, so Duo Survival incorporates cooperative play into these sessions in a slightly different way. One different thing about this game is that you and your client are playing at the same time, whereas most cooperative board games involve taking turns. This can streamline gameplay a little bit, but it means that you are not working on that specific skill in this game.

If you get really stuck, walkthroughs and tutorials are available, and you and your client can practice seeking help as you play.

Setup: There are three versions of Duo Survival. Unless my client makes a specific request, I typically start with the original, as these levels are the easiest to clear. If the game starts off as too difficult, children tend to get discouraged and quit.

The links for Duo Survival are:

1. https://poki.com/en/g/duo-survival

2. https://poki.com/en/g/duo-survival-2

3. https://poki.com/en/g/duo-survival-3

Pull up the version you will use in your session and share your screen with your client. Give the client remote control. Because the controls in this game use the keyboard, you can both simultaneously control what is happening.

The tall character moves using the up, down, left, and right arrows, and the short character moves using W, A, S, and D. I typically let my client decide which character they want to be, and I take the other one. Throughout the game, you collect gears, and you need both characters. The smaller character moves faster, jumps higher, and fits into smaller spaces, and the taller character moves heavy things, breaks through walls, and can walk through water that is too deep for the smaller one. This leads to some great discussion about different strengths and how we often need to work together to reach a goal.

Additional Notes: I never thought flash games would be part of my therapeutic toolbox, and this particular game was originally suggested to me by a client. As I was figuring out what my options were for doing telehealth, this client asked if they could show me a game they liked, and it was Duo Survival. This just shows how important it is to keep an open mind in our work!

There is a similar game called Fire Boy and Water Girl, in which a fire character and a water character work together to get through the levels. You set it up with the same controls as Duo Survival, and it incorporates the same cooperative play, with the two characters helping each other get through each level and relying on each other's strengths. There are five versions available:

1. The Forest Temple:
   https://www.crazygames.com/game/fireboy-and-watergirl-the-forest-temple

2. *The Light Temple:*
   https://www.coolmathgames.com/0-fireboy-watergirl-2-light-temple

3. *The Ice Temple:*
   https://www.coolmathgames.com/0-fireboy-watergirl-3-ice-temple

4. *The Crystal Temple:*
   https://www.coolmathgames.com/0-fireboy-watergirl-4-crystal-temple

5. *Elements:*
   https://www.coolmathgames.com/0-fireboy-watergirl-5-elements

Foosball

Suggested Age Group: 8 and up

Therapeutic Benefits: Attention, planning, frustration tolerance, winning/losing well

Telehealth Benefits: Foosball is a fun and exciting game for a lot of kids, but I do not have the space to keep the large table in my office. When I worked in an inpatient setting, though, there were foosball and pool tables that kids could get permission to use at certain times. I noticed that some kids really opened up about their mental health struggles while playing the game.

A great thing about telehealth is that the games I can provide in this setting do not take up any physical space, so when I can find a virtual version of something that might be too large or impractical for an in-person session, I can expand my telehealth options even more.

The foosball game takes up enough of my client's attention that they feel less anxious about talking to me about presenting issues. They become engrossed in the game, but it does not take up so much of their focus that they cannot also have a conversation.

Therapy Suggestions: Have the client share a time they overcame a challenge when they score, and a time they struggled when you score.

Setup: Go to https://www.crazygames.com/game/foosball, click "play now," and click the icon of two hands shaking. Select "human versus human." Share your screen, grant remote control, and you and the client can play together using your keyboards. Red is controlled by the up/down arrows, and blue is controlled by W and S. Your players kick automatically when the ball comes into contact.

Additional Notes: It is relatively easy to carry on a conversation while playing foosball, and kids have a lot of fun with this game. You can incorporate therapeutic questions as you play or simply use the game to reduce their anxiety about the session and allow them to open up about issues related to their presenting problem, their treatment plan, or whatever happens to be on their mind that day.

Go Fish

Suggested Age Group: 5 and up

Therapeutic Benefits: Communication skills, taking turns, listening, working memory

Telehealth Benefits: Go Fish is a simple card game that most kids know how to play, and it is very easy to teach. Like other card games, its simplicity gives the client something to focus on and frees their brain up to engage in talk therapy. Although you respond to each other in the game, the coding prevents cheating or mistakes. (For example, if you ask if I have any 3s and I do, the game will tell me I'm making an error if I click "go fish.") The website that I use for this game has you collect sets of four rather than two, so there is the added working memory task of trying to recall what is in your opponent's hand.

Therapy Suggestions:

1. Give a category to each suit. For example:

- *Hearts are feelings.* When you give your opponent a heart card, name a feeling and share a time you've felt that way.
  - *Clubs are thoughts.* Name a thought you had recently that was not helpful, and share how you know it was not helpful.

  - *Spades are choices.* Name a choice you made recently that had negative consequences.

  - *Diamonds are rewards.* Name a reward you earned recently and how you earned it.

2. Get your body moving with the game! If you are asking for a numbered card, do that number of jumping jacks (or push-ups, sit-ups, etc.) or that many seconds of a body stretch.

3. Give a question to each number or face, and when you get all four of that number, you have to answer that question. For example:

- *Aces:* What is something you are good at?

- *2s:* What is something you need help with?

- *3s:* What is something you enjoy doing?

- *4s:* What is your least favorite chore and why?

- *5s:* Who is someone you admire?

- *6s:* What do you wish you could change about yourself?

- *7s:* What is something that makes you angry?

- *8s:* Where is your favorite place you have ever been?

- *9s:* Say something kind about another player.

- *10s:* What is something that calms you down?

- *Jacks:* What is something that scares you?

- *Queens:* If you were in charge, what would you change about the world?

- *Kings:* If you could be any animal, what animal would you be and why?

Setup: Go to https://cardgames.io/gofish/ and select "multiplayer." Click "create a private table" and send the link to your client. When they join the table, the game starts. You are prompted when it is your turn to choose one of the cards in your hand to see if your opponent has any of that card.

Additional Notes: I love simple card games as a rapport-building activity—if a child is unsure about coming to therapy, I will introduce this game to put them at ease. Typically, I start with just the game so that they become more comfortable talking to me, and then add therapeutic questions later on, but you can decide what the best fit for each child is.

Grabble

Suggested Age Group: 10 and up

Therapeutic Benefits: Attention, executive functioning, problem solving, cognitive flexibility

Telehealth Benefits: This is a fun word game you can play with a client over telehealth. The computer automatically generates letters, and the game continues for as long as you choose or until you have played 98 tiles. This game gets clients thinking and engages the frontal lobe since it's a verbal activity.

Therapy Suggestions: If you would like, you can take turns with the client naming something in a therapeutic category for each letter generated while you wait for more tiles to appear. Prompts could include emotions or coping skills, or you could choose a "fun" category like types of candy if you want to use this activity for rapport building.

Setup: Go to https://www.coolmathgames.com/0-grabble and select "create a private game." The website will give you a private link to send your client. Rooms support up to six players, so you can play this game with an individual client or with a group.

Once the client enters the room, you can start the game. The computer automatically adds a letter tile to the room every few seconds, and as you submit words, those tiles disappear. This gives the game a competitive component. You can decide to "go easy" on your client or make the game more challenging to engage real-time frustration tolerance and emotion regulation.

Additional Notes: There is not a physical version of Grabble, so this is a game that I discovered after I started doing telehealth. If a child is transitioning from in-person to telehealth sessions, offering games that are not available in person can help them transition, as they feel like they get more options by doing telehealth. This game engages their brain and makes them think, and it is a fun challenge.

Guess Who

Suggested Age Group: 7 and up

Therapeutic Benefits: Listening, problem solving, taking turns, frustration tolerance, making choices, exploration of emotions

Telehealth Benefits: In the online version of Guess Who, the game provides questions for you, which ensures that the questions have definitive "yes" or "no" answers. You still answer your opponent's questions, but the game makes sure you give the correct answer, preventing cheating. Since you click the question you want to ask, you can easily talk through something while playing. Because of the way the game is presented, clients must be able to read in order to play this game. Clients also get to choose which character they want to be in the game instead of selecting randomly.

Therapy Suggestions: Choose different characters on the board, and examine their faces. Explore what each character might be thinking and feeling, and make guesses about their personalities, likes, and dislikes. After a round, ask why your client chose the character they selected. You can ask things like "What do you have in common with that character?" or "What do you like about them?"

Setup: If you and the client both own the Guess Who board game, you could play with the physical boards the same way that you would in your office. This gives the activity more of an in-person feel but negates some of the advantages of telehealth, like smoother conversation during gameplay.

To play the online version, go to https://www.crazygames.com/game/guess-who-multiplayer and select "play now," then "start." Click the play button with a globe on it and choose a nickname. Click "create a match," and name the room something your client can recognize. I recommend also choosing a simple password to ensure that only your client joins the game. Have your client navigate to the same website, follow the same steps, and then select the room you created. When they enter the password, the game will begin.

Additional Notes: Many young kids love guessing games, and Guess Who is one that most are familiar with. As with many therapeutic telehealth games, the activity lends itself to talk-based interventions that can be implemented simultaneously as you play the game. Since you get to choose your character, the online version lends itself to even more exploration.

Hexxagon

Suggested Age Group: 6 and up

Therapeutic Benefits: Executive functioning, planning, taking turns, consequences

Therapy Suggestions: Create a list of categories, and name things from each category based on how many gems you spawn each turn. The categories can include emotions, coping skills, things that make you feel happy, and so on.

Setup: Go to https://hexxagon.com/, choose "player vs. player," and share your screen. You and your client will take turns controlling the screen to play the game. When you move a gem to a space adjacent to it, the gem spawns or replicates itself. When a gem lands next to opponent gems, it converts each adjacent gem to its own color. When the board is full, the winner is the player with the most gems.

Additional Notes: I was a big fan of Hexxagon back in the early 2000s, though I usually played against the computer. It was challenging and helped me learn to strategize and plan ahead. Though Hexxagon does not have a physical version that I know of, it is similar to the game Othello, with each player trying to have the most pieces by the time no more moves are available. Kids like that they can play a "computer game" during their therapy time, and the skills needed to play this game fit into many kids' treatment plans.

Jigsaw Puzzles

Suggested Age Group: 3 and up

Therapeutic Benefits: Problem solving, frustration tolerance, teamwork, asking for help

Telehealth Benefits: Lots of kids like puzzles, but they get bored with the limited options available in my office. The website I use for online jigsaw puzzles has new images posted every day, and there is an option to automatically generate a puzzle from an image that you upload, giving you infinite choices. It also gives you the option to choose how many pieces the puzzle has, so you can tailor the intervention to the age and developmental level of each client.

Therapy Suggestions: Start and end the puzzle activity with a mindfulness activity. You can also choose a prompt to answer each time you find pieces that go together, like naming an emotion or sharing something you are good at.

Setup: Go to https://www.jigsawexplorer.com/ and select the puzzle you want to do. If you plan to make a custom puzzle, choose any puzzle for now (you can change it later). Click "play this puzzle." The game will open with four options in the center of the screen: "choose the number of puzzle pieces," "make the puzzle pieces rotatable," "change the background color," and "multiplayer mode." You can share the room with the client by making a custom link when you select multiplayer mode, and you and the client can move pieces around simultaneously in this mode.

In the upper-left corner of the screen, there are three lines. Click on them to see the option to create a custom puzzle with your own image. If you choose to upload your own image, you cannot enter multiplayer mode. However, you and the client can still work on the puzzle together using screen sharing and taking turns.

Additional Notes: There are so many options to implement a jigsaw puzzle in your telehealth session, and clients have so much fun deciding which puzzle to complete and how many pieces they want to sort through, and even creating their own puzzles with images from family vacations or other things that are important to them. Along with the skills built through the puzzle activities, these added features open the activity up to even more conversation and emotion exploration.

Ludo

Suggested Age Group: 6 and up

Therapeutic Benefits: Taking turns, frustration tolerance, exploration of emotions, safety planning, conflict resolution

Telehealth Benefits: As with many telehealth games, Ludo enforces the rules, so you can practice setting different boundaries without sacrificing rapport if a child has difficulty letting go of control. The game also allows you to add players controlled by the computer—I have had kids ask for stuffed animals or imaginary friends to join us in the game, and with the computer feature, these added players take their own turns.

Therapy Suggestions: Ludo is an old board game that is basically a predecessor to games like Sorry and Trouble. If you are familiar with these games, you know that the object is to get all four of your pieces around the board and safely home before your opponent. In Sorry, your piece can enter the "safety zone" before it reaches home, and your piece cannot be sent back to start once it is in the safety zone. I like to use this component of the game to talk about "safety zones" in real life. Where can you go that you have privacy, and others are not supposed to intrude?

Ludo has certain places on the board that are also "safe," where you and your opponent can both place a piece at the same time with neither piece getting sent back to start. This becomes an analogy for how we might need to hit "pause" in a disagreement before coming back to solve the problem.

Setup: Go to https://www.coolmathgames.com/0-ludo and select "play." You can have two to four players, with you and the client each selected as humans. If desired, you can add computer players. Click "start." Share the screen with your client, and take turns with screen control to move your pieces.

Additional Notes: Before transitioning to telehealth, I used Sorry as a therapy game to get kids talking about safety. The game presents a nonthreatening way to bring up the topic of safety. Although I was not familiar with Ludo, I was glad to learn that something very similar was available for telehealth.

Mancala

Suggested Age Group: 4 and up

Therapeutic Benefits: Taking turns, planning, focus

Telehealth Benefits: Who goes first is randomized, so you take turns starting. Kids with fine motor deficits benefit from using this game over telehealth, since they simply click or tap on the pile of pieces that they would like to move and do not have to physically place pieces in each spot. The game also keeps count of the pieces for you, which simplifies the process somewhat.

Setup: Go to https://mancala.playdrift.com/ and select "new game," "private," then "create room." Send the link to your client. When you are both in the room, you will see a countdown. If you both select "ready," it counts down from five and starts the game. Take turns choosing which pieces to move around the board, and try to get pieces in your bank. When there are no pieces left on the board, the person with the most in their bank wins.

Additional Notes: I had Mancala available in my office for years, and it was almost never chosen, but when I switched to telehealth, it was one of the most asked-for games in my sessions for a while. Kids seem to like the simplicity, and it is a quick game that you can play several times over if you would like. It has a timer feature, but it does not penalize you if the time runs out, so you can work on time anxiety without having the child become frustrated if they run out of time.

Match Up

Suggested Age Group: 3 and up

Therapeutic Benefits: Executive functioning, working memory, taking turns, frustration tolerance, focus, exploration of emotions

Telehealth Benefits: Because you are using a computer screen, the cards stay organized much more easily than in person. You can calculate things like how many turns it takes to get through levels, and you can adjust the difficulty level easily.

Therapy Suggestions: Use mindfulness to process emotions brought up when the client successfully finds a match or when they have difficulty finding a match. Have the client say a positive thing about themselves when they find a match.

Setup: There are many online memory games; the one that I prefer to use is https://www.helpfulgames.com/subjects/brain-training/memory.html because you get to choose how many cards there are in each round. Go to the website, select a level from 1 to 6 (12 cards to 36 cards), and share your screen with your client. Take turns trying to find matches. Since this website assumes you are playing by yourself, it does not keep score, which can reduce competitiveness.

Additional Notes: Match Up is a simple game that most kids understand pretty easily. It can help them practice executive functioning and working memory skills, which can be beneficial in settings outside of the session. It's a great game to make available in sessions, since the difficulty level can be adjusted for various age groups.

Pictionary

Suggested Age Group: 7 and up

Therapeutic Benefits: Frustration tolerance, communication skills, exploration of emotions, perfectionism

Telehealth Benefits: The website used for this game gives a time limit, which helps with working through anxiety about timed tasks without the therapist having to impose this. It also gives three prompts to choose from, so the client gets to decide what they are going to draw but does not have to come up with ideas on their own. As the time ticks down, the game gives you hints that can help you guess.

Therapy Suggestions: The website that I use for Pictionary in telehealth has an option to add custom words, but I have found that the custom words tend to not pop up as options unless I select "use custom words exclusively." This is an option, but you want to make sure you have a long enough list of words. I recommend using different emotions, coping skills, and words related to the client's interests, history, and treatment plan.

Setup: Telehealth Pictionary can be played using the whiteboard on your telehealth platform, but I prefer to use https://skribbl.io/ because it generates prompts and time limits for you. Go to the site, choose a nickname, design your avatar, and then click "create private room." At the bottom of the screen, you will see an option to "invite your friends." Copy the link and send it to your client.

You can decide how many rounds you want to play, between two and ten, with time limits ranging from 30 seconds to three minutes. This means that this game can be a fun reward if there are specific interventions you want to get through. You can let your client know that the number of rounds you are going to play together depends on how much time is left when you finish the things you need to do.

Using the Skribbl platform, you choose from three prompts that the site presents to you, and you have to type your answers into the chat to win rounds. This means that this version of Pictionary can only be played with clients who are old enough to read prompts and type their answers. (Again, younger clients could simply use the whiteboard feature to play this game, but then they have to come up with their own prompts each round.) You can give them the option to state their guesses out loud, but this means you have to wait until the timer runs out for the round to end.

Additional Notes: Pictionary is a great game for kids with perfectionistic tendencies because the goal of the game is to make a drawing that is accurate enough for the other players to recognize, not a drawing that is perfect. Incorporating therapeutic prompts is a great way to get kids talking about things related to their treatment plans, and guessing is so much fun!

Scattergories

Suggested Age Group: 8 and up

Therapeutic Benefits: Problem solving, creative thinking, cognitive flexibility, frustration tolerance

Telehealth Benefits: Prompts are automatically generated, and you can choose from hundreds of categories or create your own. The time length is up to you, as well as the number of categories. When you finish a round, you and your opponent can debate whether certain things "fit" into the category.

Setup: Go to https://scattergoriesonline.net/new-game.xhtml to create a new game. This is the one telehealth game website where I created a free account because you can create your own categories if you are logged in. When you go to the site, you are given automatically generated categories. You need to check which categories are selected, as some that automatically generate are not child-appropriate (for example, "things you do when you're drunk"), but you can choose categories that are appropriate and create some that fit with the child's treatment plan. I like to use "emotions," "things that make me sad," "things that scare me," "things I like," and similar options. You can use just a few categories or add more if desired.

This game can be played with a time limit, which you can choose based on how many categories you want to use, or you can have the game go until you press "stop." Typically, I ask clients what they prefer. You can also select which letters will come up, and you might decide to eliminate some more difficult letters depending on the client.

Additional Notes: Scattergories has been a lot of fun to use in sessions, and it gets kids thinking creatively. I love how easy it is to tailor categories to incorporate each client's interests and treatment goals. It gets kids talking but still falls into the category of a game, so those who are a bit hesitant about therapy can still enjoy it.

Snakes and Ladders

Suggested Age Group: 3 and up

Therapeutic Benefits: Frustration tolerance, taking turns, actions and consequences, emotion regulation

Telehealth Benefits: The most helpful part of playing this game over telehealth is that the game keeps track of how many spaces you need to go and in which direction. Although this is a simple game that does not require any reading, young kids often have trouble with tracking the numbered spaces, and the telehealth version eliminates this aspect. It also moves up the ladders and down the snakes automatically, so you can work through emotions that come up when this happens.

Therapy Suggestions: Snakes and Ladders is a great game for learning about choices and consequences. Although the online version does not show scenarios on the squares like the physical board game, you can still explore choices that lead to good consequences and choices that lead to consequences the child might not want. You can ask the client to talk about recent experiences when they have felt like they went up a small or big ladder, or down a small or big snake.

Setup: Go to https://toytheater.com/snakes-and-ladders/, click "play," click "human vs. human," and select the number of players. Share your screen with your client to let them pick what color their piece will be. Select "play," then take turns rolling the dice. The game moves for you based on what you roll. When you land at the bottom of a ladder, you get to climb that ladder, and when you land at the top of a snake, you slide down the snake.

Additional Notes: This is another game that most kids are familiar with, so being able to introduce it in a session can help kids feel more comfortable meeting with me. I love how telehealth games with rules coded in can bring out emotions that you might not see in an in-person, nondirective session. This is a great game for building rapport that can simultaneously bring up themes from the child's treatment plan.

Tic Tac Toe

Suggested Age Group: 3 and up

Therapeutic Benefits: Planning, problem solving, frustration tolerance

Telehealth Benefits: Tic Tac Toe is a simple game that most kids know how to play or can learn fairly quickly. Although this game could easily be incorporated into any session, it is not something I used with any frequency prior to transitioning to telehealth. Then, when I first began working from home and was figuring out what games I could play with kids online, quite a few suggested it. I think it was a nonthreatening, simple game they could incorporate into their sessions. It incorporates some skill building, and it gives the child something to focus on to reduce their anxiety about the session itself.

Setup: You can play Tic Tac Toe using a whiteboard by simply drawing the three-by-three board and taking turns drawing x's and o's. If the child is having trouble drawing on the whiteboard, you can label the boxes with numbers one through nine and have them tell you which box they selected—this adds an opportunity to work on communication skills.

You can also play Tic Tac Toe on this website: https://www.crazygames.com/game/tic-tac-toe. Select "play now," "start," and then the "play" icon with a globe. Enter a nickname and click "create match." I recommend using a simple password to ensure that your client is the only one who can join your game. Share the link with your client, and have them follow the same steps that you did up until "create match." Instead of creating a match, the client will see your nickname on the list of available games. They can enter the password and join you in the private game room.

The website gives you the option to play three-by-three, five-by-five, or seven-by-seven boards. The larger boards require four in a row to win instead of three, which is a fun added challenge and makes the game enjoyable for kids who might feel that they are a bit old for classic Tic Tac Toe.

Trivia

Suggested Age Group: 10 and up

Therapeutic Benefits: Communication skills, focus, problem solving, frustration tolerance, emotion regulation, cooperative play

Telehealth Benefits: Trivia games are a great way to get kids talking in sessions without pushing for any difficult or scary topics they might not feel comfortable discussing. The online version that I use does not let you and your client play against each other; instead, you are playing as a team against a bot. Having this "common enemy" fosters rapport between you and your client as you work together to figure out the answers. The game generates questions as you go and keeps score.

Therapy Suggestions: Trivia questions may come up that are related to the client's interests. Use this as an opportunity to make a connection. You can also process frustration in real time as difficult questions come up or when the client gets the wrong answer.

Setup: Go to https://www.memory-improvement-tips.com/free-trivial-pursuit-window. html and share your screen. Click "play," "click to start," and "play." Select "play with bot" (the other option pairs you with a stranger). You can have the client tell you which answers to select as a way to work on communication skills, or you can grant screen control and take turns choosing answers.

Additional Notes: This is a great activity to build rapport in a nonthreatening way. Some of the questions are difficult even for me, so I get to model for kids how we can handle our frustration when we do not know an answer. Trivia questions are not something I had used in my in-person sessions, so this is an example of something new that came from doing telehealth sessions.

Tumbling Tower

Suggested Age Group: 6 and up

Therapeutic Benefits: Mindfulness, patience, emotion regulation, fine motor skills

Telehealth Benefits: My favorite thing about Tumbling Tower on telehealth is what I love about many telehealth games: no cleanup. Kids with sensory issues appreciate that the blocks are quiet when they fall down, and no time is spent resetting the tower.

Therapy Suggestions: The site that I use for this game has downloadable question lists for anger, emotional well-being, and young persons. Of course, you can always make your own questions list too. When you pull a block, you answer the question with the corresponding number. Many of us use the questions stickers on our physical tumbling tower blocks, but these numbered blocks mean that you can have multiple question sets for different ages or presenting problems.

Setup: Go to https://watotoplay.com/tumbling-tower/ and scroll down to the tower graphic. Share your screen with the client, and take turns with screen control to pull pieces. When the tower falls, simply refresh the screen to start the game over.

Additional Notes: Kids have a bit of a learning curve when it comes to manipulating the blocks in this version of Tumbling Tower, but they are so proud of themselves when they figure it out! The activity can be therapeutic on its own, but the added option to work in questions makes this a great way to start conversations related to treatment goals.

Uno

Suggested Age Group: 5 and up

Therapeutic Benefits: Focus, planning, frustration tolerance, taking turns

Telehealth Benefits: Although the game still enforces some rules, thus setting boundaries, there is flexibility that allows the client to have control over what some of these rules are. You can choose to draw even if you could play, so you can let the client win if that is most appropriate in the moment. When it's your turn, the game highlights which cards you could choose to play, so kids who are still learning the rules get instructions without having to show you their cards.

Therapy Suggestions: Choose a category for each color. For example:

1. Red: Share something you did today

2. Blue: Share a feeling you had today

3. Yellow: Share a thought you had today

4. Green: Share something you like about yourself

Or choose a feeling for each color and share a time you had that feeling. For example:

1. Red: Angry

2. Blue: Sad

3. Yellow: Scared

4. Green: Happy

Setup: Go to https://play.unofreak.com/, select "join a game (play)," and create your room. I recommend setting a password; the client will not need to enter it to join the game, but it keeps strangers from trying to join your game. I select "random player order" so that we take turns going first and "hide from lobby," again to prevent anyone else from trying to join the game. You can decide whether you want to allow stacking (placing a Draw 2 on top of a Draw 2 instead of drawing) and doubles (placing two identical cards in one turn), as well as how many cards you want to start with. You can start with up to 50 cards, though I do not recommend going that high, as the game freezes if you run out of cards.

Once you have selected your settings, click "create game," send the link to your client, and start the game when they join.

You can also play Uno if you and the client both have physical decks by holding up your choice to the camera, with each of you drawing from your own deck.

Additional Notes: I'm pretty sure the ethics code has a rule that you aren't a real child therapist unless you play Uno at least once a day. As with other card games, Uno is great for building rapport, and it can help distract kids from their anxiety about coming to therapy, which can allow them to open up more. This is a familiar and popular game across age groups.

Yahtzee

Suggested Age Group: 8 and up

Therapeutic Benefits: Focus, problem solving, frustration tolerance, taking turns

Telehealth Benefits: This is a fun, classic game that many kids are familiar with, and scoring requires a lot of attention. You can help your client with this, or they can problem solve it themselves. A game of Yahtzee tends to take your full attention, so this is a good way to build your relationship with the client early in therapy.

Setup: If you and your client each have five dice, you can play Yahtzee over telehealth this way. Otherwise, you can go to https://www.elversonpuzzle.com/yahtzee-dice-roller.html and share your screen. The website has a set of five dice, and you can decide which to roll and which to hold. The rules are not coded into the site, so you have the option to let the client change the rules if you are taking a nondirective approach.

Free score sheets are available here: https://www.memory-improvement-tips.com/yahtzee-score-sheets.html

One reason why I love incorporating art into therapy sessions is that art allows us to process feelings without using words. When the amygdala (emotion center of the brain) is activated, the frontal lobe (the area that controls impulse control, judgment, and language) powers down. There are times when it is important to get the frontal lobe up and running as quickly as possible, but other times it is beneficial to allow clients to process their feelings nonverbally so they can experience those emotions more fully. Art gives clients that outlet without having to get the talking part of the brain back online.

There are different ways you can do art over telehealth:

1. You and your client can each use traditional art supplies. Some clients like this because they can decide when and how much of their work I see.

2. You can use the whiteboard feature on your telehealth platform or https://r8.whiteboardfox.com/ to draw together or observe as the client draws. Go to the site and click "start drawing," then "create whiteboard." There is a paid version of this site, but you can do drawing activities for free. This gives you the client's visual perspective as they work on the drawing, which means any projective drawings give you even more information! Erasing is easy, and colors never run out.

3. You can screen share Microsoft Paint and grant the client remote control of your screen to draw. Although you can't both draw at the same time if you use this tactic, it gives the same perspective as the whiteboards and more color options. As with the whiteboard option, you can erase and never run out of a color.

4. If the client is on a tablet, they can screen share apps like Procreate and show you their art as they create it.

If you have some drawing prompts that you already use with clients, you can certainly use the methods I just listed to adapt your existing activities to telehealth or to come up with new ones. In addition, the following pages present 17 art-based activities with instructions for easy implementation in a telehealth setting.

Auto Draw

Suggested Age Group: 6 and up

Therapeutic Benefits: Mindfulness, exploration of emotions, perfectionism

Telehealth Benefits: This website guesses what you are trying to draw based on the lines you make, so it could be seen as similar to Pictionary with the computer making guesses. It is so satisfying to let the computer polish the drawings you made. Kids who get frustrated with drawing tasks due to perfectionistic tendencies like this platform because it makes the drawing task easier for them.

Setup: Go to https://www.autodraw.com/ and share your screen with your client. Let them have screen control. This platform can be used with various drawing prompts or for nondirective art therapy.

Questions:

1. What options do you see for what that drawing could be? What do those things have in common? How are they different?

2. How would it change the drawing if you chose different images from those suggestions?

3. How does it feel when the computer "touches up" your drawing?

Camping Trip Drawing:
Joint Drawing Task

Suggested Age Group: 8 and up

Therapeutic Benefits: Mindfulness and relaxation, exploration of emotions, exploration of relationship patterns, communication skills

Telehealth Benefits: Both (or all) participants can draw simultaneously without getting in each other's way and can easily interact with components of each other's drawings.

Setup: Once you have your whiteboard set up, you can introduce the task to your client by telling them, "Today I have an activity that we can do together. We are going to work on a drawing at the same time and help each other." You can work on the drawing with your client, or if it is a family session, you can observe as they work on it together. The act of creating the drawing generates communication and discussion around the prompt.

Prompt: "Draw two people on a camping trip together. Draw them both in the campsite together doing something. Draw what the weather is like."

Questions:

1. Who are these people?

2. What are they doing, and how do they feel?

3. Why did they decide to go camping, and where are they?

4. What is the weather like in this picture?

5. If you were on this camping trip, what would you be doing?

Draw a Garden:
Joint Drawing Task

Suggested Age Group: 6 and up

Therapeutic Benefits: Mindfulness and relaxation, exploration of emotions, creativity, communication skills

Telehealth Benefits: You can see your client's drawing from their perspective as they create it, which shows you how they approach the task, the order in which everything is drawn, and how they prioritize the parts of the drawing.

Setup: You can do this drawing with your client, have them work on the drawing with a family member or members, or use this activity with a group. If you choose to use this activity individually and have the client do the drawing task alone, you can simply skip to the prompt.

If you are doing the activity as part of a family therapy session or in a group, you can introduce the activity to everyone at once. Once you have your whiteboard set up, introduce the task: "Today I have an activity that we can do together. We are going to work on a drawing at the same time and help each other."

Prompt: "Draw a garden that includes dirt, plants, and someone tending to it."

Questions:

1. Where is this garden?

2. Tell me about the plants. What kind of plants are they?

3. Who is the gardener?

4. Does the gardener do a good job taking care of the garden?

5. How did they decide which plants to put in the garden?

6. What does the garden need to thrive?

Draw Your Family

Suggested Age Group: 4 and up

Therapeutic Benefits: Exploration of relationship patterns, communication skills, exploration of emotions

Telehealth Benefits: You can see the drawing as the client makes it from their own perspective. This task is relatively easy to complete, and most kids find the prompt nonthreatening.

Setup: Set up the whiteboard and let the client know that you would like them to do some drawing today. Let them know that there is no right or wrong response, and they can interpret the prompt in whatever way feels right for them. Ask them to let you know when they are finished drawing.

Prompt: "Please draw your family doing something, and remember to include yourself. Make sure to show how each person is feeling by drawing it on their face."

Questions:

1. Who is each person?

2. What is each of them doing?

3. What is each of them feeling?

4. *If any family member is left out:* Where is _____?

5. What makes your family get along?

6. What makes your family disagree?

7. What do you like about your family?

8. What would you change if you could?

Draw Your Feelings

Suggested Age Group: 3 and up

Therapeutic Benefits: Exploration of emotions, mindfulness, communication skills

Telehealth Benefits: I have found that kids' inhibitions tend to lower when making feelings drawings using the telehealth whiteboard because they know they can erase things with a single click. Kids also like that they cannot run out of a color and that they can more freely express themselves without making a mess that needs to be cleaned up before your next session.

Setup: You can use either a blank whiteboard or the body outline (provided next) for this activity. Upload the image to the whiteboard, or screen share the image and allow the client to annotate on your screen. The blank whiteboard allows the child to take a more open-ended approach to the prompt, but the body outline helps the child communicate what their experience of the feeling is inside of their body.

Prompt: "I want you to draw how you are feeling right now in this moment. Is your feeling big or small? What color or colors is it? What shape is it, and what does it look like?"

Questions:

1. What feeling words do you associate with this picture?

2. Do you like having this feeling?

3. What other times have you felt this way?

4. If you could control the feeling, what would you change about it?

5. Where do you experience this feeling in your body?

6. How can you let people know when you feel this way?

Draw Your Home

Suggested Age Group: 3 and up

Therapeutic Benefits: Exploration of emotions, exploration of relationships, mindfulness and relaxation

Telehealth Benefits: Watching the approach your client takes to this task provides a lot of information about their home and their relationships with the different people in it. Since clients can erase, you get to view things they might include as they are working on the drawing but do not leave in as part of the final drawing.

Setup: Set up your preferred whiteboard and give the child the prompt. You can ask questions as they work on the drawing or wait until they are finished.

Prompt: "Today I want you to draw where you live. Draw what it looks like on the inside and on the outside."

Questions:

1. Who lives here? How does everyone who lives here fit into the home?

2. What part is your favorite place to be? Why?

3. What do you like about where you live?

4. What would you change about this place if you could?

5. What does this place need to keep everyone safe?

6. Where do you go when you feel sad?

7. Where do you go when you feel angry?

8. Where do you go when you feel scared?

Etch A Sketch

Suggested Age Group: 3 and up

Therapeutic Benefits: Mindfulness and relaxation, perfectionism, nondirective art, exploration of emotions

Telehealth Benefits: You will not accidentally shake the Etch A Sketch and erase your work before you meant to! You also get to see what your client is making as they make it.

Setup: Several virtual Etch A Sketches are available. One can be found at https://scratch.mit.edu/projects/239506/. Pull up the site and share your screen with the client, then give them remote control so they can work on their drawing. You can prompt them to try to draw certain things, but this intervention also works with a more nondirective approach.

Optional Prompt: "I want you to use this to draw your feeling when _____." You can choose feelings prompts like "when you feel angry/upset/sad/scared" or triggers like "when you have to do homework/when someone yells." After the client finishes their drawing, shake away the difficult feeling!

Questions:

1. How do you feel when doing this activity?

2. How is this different from drawing on paper or on other websites?

3. How do you feel when the thing you don't like disappears?

Fear Drawing

Suggested Age Group: 3 and up

Therapeutic Benefits: Exploration of emotions, mindfulness and relaxation, exploration of coping skills

Telehealth Benefits: As with the other telehealth drawing activities, clients are more engaged and vulnerable in this task knowing they can erase as they go if they want to. Clients will not run out of a color halfway through, which is helpful for this activity in particular—there will be no interruption to the creative process due to a crayon breaking or a marker going dry.

Setup: Prepare the whiteboard, then give the child the prompt. You can narrate as the child works on their drawing or let them work in silence. When the activity is finished, you can give the client the option to save the picture or erase it to show how they have overcome their fear.

Prompt: "Now I would like you to do something that might be a little bit difficult. I want you to draw what fear looks like for you. This could mean drawing what you look like when you are afraid, what scares you the most, or something abstract with colors and lines that remind you of fear. Remember, there is no wrong way to do this activity."

Questions:

1. What was it like for you to do this activity?

2. What were you thinking about while you made your drawing?

3. What does fear mean to you?

4. What does bravery mean to you?

5. What should we do with your fear today?

Mandala Drawing

Suggested Age Group: 10 and up

Therapeutic Benefits: Mindfulness and relaxation, exploration of emotions, identification of needs

Telehealth Benefits: You can watch the client create their drawing from the client's perspective in real time and narrate the activity as they complete their drawing.

Setup: Once you have your whiteboard set up, draw a large circle. Tell your client, "A mandala is a circle that we draw patterns in. There is no right or wrong way to do the mandala, but I hope that it helps you feel really relaxed."

Prompt: "Fill the circle with what relaxes you. You can draw something specific, like things from nature, or just make colors and shapes that you find peaceful and calming."

Questions (can be incorporated during the activity or asked afterward):

1. How do you feel while you're drawing the mandala?

2. What images (colors, lines, etc.) are you including?

3. When are times that the relaxation you are feeling right now might help you in your life?

After the drawing is done, you can teach your client to draw circles in the air with their finger to make imaginary mandalas any time they feel stressed out, anxious, or upset.

Origami/Paper Folding

Suggested Age Group: 10 and up

Therapeutic Benefits: Mindfulness and relaxation, frustration tolerance, problem solving, creativity, communication skills, following directions

Telehealth Benefits: Origami is a great mindfulness activity for sessions, and clients can bring their cool creations home with them. In person, kids often ask me to help them, which is a great way to work on communication skills; however, when I am in a telehealth session, I do not have the option to intervene physically, so kids have to work through their frustration on their own (or if the caregiver is participating in the session, you can have the client practice asking for and receiving help from their caregiver).

Setup: This activity requires the client to have paper on hand. Printer paper or even notebook paper can work for this activity, as long as the client is able to cut the paper into a square. Printer-sized paper can also work for making paper airplanes if that is more in line with the client's interests.

If clients have experience with this kind of activity, they might want to teach you how to make something, which can be good for practicing communication. You can learn a new skill together too. There are hundreds of tutorial videos on YouTube; you can search based on what the client wants to create and how difficult the project is. Share your screen and audio, and follow the steps together.

When the client is having a hard time with the activity, you can work through frustration and problem solve together while practicing coping skills and monitoring their effectiveness in real time.

When the project is finished, there will be differences between your creation and the one your client created. This might be an opportunity to address confidence if the client feels like yours is better than theirs. You can also talk about how the two designs are different even though you followed the same steps, just like every person is unique.

Questions:
1. How did you feel when you were working on this activity?
2. What was it like for you when you were having a hard time with the project?
3. How did you feel when you overcame the hard part?
4. How does your final project look different from mine? How do they look similar?

Safe Place Drawing

Suggested Age Group: 6 and up

Therapeutic Benefits: Exploration of emotions, exploration of coping, communication skills, mindfulness and relaxation, safety planning

Telehealth Benefits: Seeing the order that the client chooses for completing this task shows you which aspects of their safe space are most important to them.

Setup: Prepare your whiteboard and introduce the task. When the project is finished, save it and send the client a copy so they can remember their safe space when they are having a hard time.

Prompt: "Imagine that you feel very safe and secure, the safest you have felt in your entire life. Now imagine where you are. It could be a place you've been in real life, a fictional place from a story, or somewhere that you made up! I want you to draw this place with as much detail as you can imagine."

Questions:

1. Where is this place?

2. What kinds of things are in the safe place that you couldn't draw? What does it sound like, smell like, and feel like?

3. Is this a real place, or are parts of it inspired by a real place?

After the client finishes their drawing, have them close their eyes and imagine that they are in their safe place. Have them think about what they can see, hear, smell, feel, and taste. Ask them to imagine as many details as they can. Let them know that they can go to their safe place in their mind any time they want to.

Sand Drawing

Suggested Age Group: 3 and up

Therapeutic Benefits: Mindfulness and relaxation, creativity, exploration of emotions

Telehealth Benefits: As therapeutic as sand work can be, it is messy! The online sand drawing provides similar relaxation benefits without getting sand everywhere. Clients can add items to decorate their sand garden, and if they want multiples of the same item, this is easy to do online.

Setup: Pull up the website https://www.agame.com/game/sand-drawing. This site lets you choose a texture of sand on a beach. You can cover your beach with seashells and other beach-related items, and you can draw in the sand using what appears to be either your finger or a stick. You can write or make drawings in the sand. And when you are finished, you can have a wave appear to wash everything away clean.

With this activity, I usually do not provide a specific prompt but let the client take a nondirective approach to their sand drawing. This can be a fun way to explore where they are at emotionally and to let them share what they are bringing to their session.

If the client wants this activity to be interactive, you can take turns controlling the screen and adding different things to the scene. You can narrate what the client includes and ask them about their feelings as they complete the task.

Sand Painting

Suggested Age Group: 6 and up

Therapeutic Benefits: Mindfulness and relaxation, cause and effect, exploration of emotions, letting go of control, working through aggression

Telehealth Benefits: This activity is part art project, part virtual science experiment. You can see how the different components (like water, plants, fire, and gunpowder) interact in various ways and create different scenes based on these interactions. The scenes created with this activity look really cool, but it is impossible to "draw" a specific way, as the program generates the reactions on its own. Therefore, clients have to be ready to let go of a certain amount of control with this activity. Clients can grow and destroy things, so the activity also lends itself to working through aggressive impulses. And of course, it would not be safe to use most of these chemicals in an in-person session!

Setup: Navigate to https://www.artsology.com/sandpainting-game2.php, share the screen with your client, and grant them remote control. If desired, the client can prompt you to help with the activity.

Prompt: "This activity lets you mix different chemicals together and see what happens. When you put some things together, things grow, and when you mix other things together, they get destroyed. Make the scene whatever you want it to be, and see what you can make happen!"

Questions:

1. Which combinations are your favorites, and what do you like about them?

2. Did you like growing or destroying things more? Why?

3. What was difficult about this activity for you?

4. What parts were hard to control?

5. How did it feel when the image was turning out differently than you pictured?

Sandscapes

Suggested Age Group: 3 and up

Therapeutic Benefits: Mindfulness and relaxation, creativity, exploration of emotions

Telehealth Benefits: Virtual sandscapes allow the mindfulness and creativity of in-person sand work without the mess. Especially with efforts to slow the spread of diseases, sand is not the cleanest option, as it is difficult (if not impossible) to sanitize. This activity lets clients get creative, and the sound of falling sand is incredibly soothing.

Setup: Navigate to https://thisissand.com/. Share your screen with the client, and grant them remote control so they can choose colors and drop the sand. They can choose a solid color or click the bull's-eye to get a random combination of colors.

Many kids like dropping the sand themselves, but some like to direct me to do it for them. Sometimes, they will use the annotate feature (available if you are using Zoom) to draw on top of the sandscape.

This activity is great for nondirective mindfulness and art work. Typically, the sand creates abstract scenes, which can be either a relaxation exercise or an opportunity to explore emotions in a projective way ("How do you feel when you look at this picture?").

Self-Portrait Drawing

Suggested Age Group: 5 and up

Therapeutic Benefits: Exploration of emotions, identity work, communication skills, mindfulness

Telehealth Benefits: As with many of the art activities presented here, doing a self-portrait over telehealth gives you your client's view of what they are creating in real time. You can see parts that they might choose to erase and not include in their final drawing.

Setup: After preparing your preferred whiteboard, use the suggested prompt to start the activity. With this activity, I recommend waiting to query until the client is finished drawing.

Prompt: "A self-portrait is a drawing that someone makes of themselves. I would like you to do a self-portrait today. Draw yourself, and take as much time as you need to."

Questions:

1. How did this activity make you feel?

2. What was it like drawing yourself? What things did you notice about yourself?

3. Were there things you chose not to include in your drawing?

4. Is there anything in your drawing that you added to yourself?

5. What would you change about your drawing?

6. What things were you glad you could include in your drawing?

7. If I told someone else to draw a picture of you, how might their drawing be different from yours?

Weave Silk

Suggested Age Group: 4 and up

Therapeutic Benefits: Mindfulness and relaxation, exploration of emotions, perfectionism

Telehealth Benefits: This activity creates a beautiful, abstract image. The website creates an image that mirrors what the client makes. It's very relaxing activity, and the abstract nature of the drawing lets kids get around perfectionistic tendencies and focus on the therapeutic benefits of the activity.

Setup: Go to http://weavesilk.com/, share your screen, and grant the client remote control. They can choose different colors, decide how many mirror points (between one and six), and draw different shapes to make a variety of designs.

If you want to make the activity more directive, you can prompt the client to draw their feelings using the colors and shapes; however, you can also take a nondirective approach.

Questions:

1. How do you feel when doing this activity?

2. What feelings would you associate with the colors that you used?

3. What is it like to make art where you don't control exactly what it will look like?

What If You Were a _____?

Suggested Age Group: 5 and up

Therapeutic Benefits: Exploration of emotions, identity work, communication skills, mindfulness

Telehealth Benefits: You can witness the child's drawing as they are creating it. You can see which things they add first, which things they choose to erase, and how much detail goes into different components of the drawing.

Setup: This activity is similar to the self-portrait but can be helpful if a child is guarded or does not have strong rapport established with you. The imaginative component of this task allows the child to distance themselves from the self-portrait because they are drawing themselves in an imaginary sense rather than a literal self-portrait.

Pull up the whiteboard and prompt the child to do the drawing activity. Wait until they are finished to present discussion questions, and you can always tweak these questions based on the child's responses and individual needs.

This prompt is deliberately open-ended. You can tell the child to draw themselves as an animal, a fictional creature, or a character of a book or show that they enjoy. Tailor it to the child's unique interests, and the child is more likely to become engaged and interested in the activity.

Prompt: "I want you to draw a picture of yourself today, but not a real picture of you as you are in real life. I want you to draw what you would look like if you were a _____."

Questions:

1. How did you feel while doing this activity?

2. How is your drawing different from you? How is it the same?

3. In what ways do you wish you were more like the "you" in the picture?

4. How could you be more like this version of you?

5. In what ways are you glad you are different from the "you" in the picture?

One big challenge when moving to online sessions with kids is that telehealth is less conducive to activities or interventions that involve movement. You and your client both need to try to stay visible in the frame, which can be difficult to focus on when you are doing an activity that involves movement. When meeting with kids in person, you can follow them as they move around the room or at least turn your head to see where they went, but over telehealth, you can only face the direction in which you are pointed by the client.

At the same time, it is especially difficult for very young kids or those with hyperactivity to sit for the duration of a session. Generally, kids need to move about once every five minutes in order to stay engaged. The activities presented in this section are intended to get kids moving while keeping them engaged with you in the session.

You might need to redirect clients to ensure that you can still see and hear them; the important part with redirection is making sure that these prompts are presented gently and in a way that is not a reprimand. I find it helpful to say, "Oh no, I can't see you when you are over there! Can you please move a bit to the left?" I communicate to kids that the reason I need to be able to see and hear them is because I care about what they have to say, and the things they want to share with me are important.

This section includes 10 activities that get clients moving, along with tips for ensuring they remain engaged in the session (and in your view on the camera) while doing them.

Body Stretches

Suggested Age Group: 3 and up

Therapeutic Benefits: Body work, impulse control, mindfulness and relaxation, communication

Telehealth Benefits: Doing stretches together gets both you and your client alert and focused on the moment. Having to be aware of where you are in relation to the frame can be a challenge, but it also helps focus both of you on the activity and maintain engagement with the session. This is a great way to help kids who need to move remain focused on the session and treatment.

Setup: There are hundreds of videos on YouTube that focus on body stretches or yoga for kids. Or you can guide the client yourself using the script below. Do the movements with your client.

Prompt: "Let's help our bodies wake up and get our muscles moving! First let's raise our hands up as high as we can, up, up, up—feel your back stretching as you reach—and count to five, 1... 2... 3... 4... 5, and down.

"Now let's turn our necks as far as we can to the right... and then to the left... and look down. Relax your head and feel how heavy it is! Next let's twist our bodies to the right, 1... 2... 3... 4... 5, and to the left, 1... 2... 3... 4... 5.

"Take your right arm and stretch it across your chest, pushing until you feel the stretch, 1... 2... 3... 4... 5, and do the same with your left arm, 1... 2... 3... 4... 5."

If the client has good balance and you are able to stand while doing this activity, you can use the following script for stretching legs:

"Lift your right knee up to your chest and hold it there with your hands. Feel the stretch in your leg, 1... 2... 3... 4... 5, and gently put your leg down. Pull your left knee to your chest and feel the stretch, 1... 2... 3... 4... 5."

You can add other stretches to this activity and help your client notice how their body feels when they engage in this activity. See what they notice as they are doing the stretches and how it changes how they are feeling.

Charades

Suggested Age Group: 5 and up

Therapeutic Benefits: Body work, impulse control, communication skills

Telehealth Benefits: This activity helps kids who might have a hard time staying still in their sessions. This game engages the client with you and helps them practice communicating things in a nonverbal way.

Setup: You can present the client with a list of options if they need help choosing something to act out. Below are some options that you can either share with them or use when it is your turn.

Prompt: "Do you know the game Charades? It's where we take turns acting things out and trying to guess what the other person is pretending to be. I have a list of things you might want to try to act out, or you can choose something yourself."

Activities	Feelings	Animals
Brushing your teeth	Happy	Cat
Washing your hands	Angry	Dog
Dancing	Sad	Fish
Opening a gift	Scared	Giraffe
Helping with chores	Frustrated	Elephant
Stretching	Annoyed	Horse
Writing	Excited	Cow
Singing	Hyper	Chicken
Running	Anxious	Crow
Juggling	Proud	Robin
Swimming	Impatient	Hippo
Talking on the phone	Calm	Bunny

You and your client can compile charade prompts based on the client's individual interests and preferences. For example, you can have the client identify things they like and dislike and list those among the prompts.

Dance Party

Suggested Age Group: 3 to 12

Therapeutic Benefits: Body work, impulse control, mindfulness, exploration of emotions, communication skills

Telehealth Benefits: This activity gets kids moving while helping them open up about different topics. You can use YouTube videos or simply audio. The balance of talking and body movement helps children engage in the session and lowers inhibitions. A great thing about doing this kind of movement work over telehealth is that kids who are self-conscious or anxious about you seeing them dance can turn off their video and participate without being seen.

Setup: If desired, you can find dance party videos on YouTube. Playfully Connected Games is one channel that has these types of videos, and I have found them very helpful in my sessions. (One activity in particular is entitled the Unicorn Game for Self-Esteem.) Each video includes music with prompts to dance and move around, as well as pauses in the music with questions and prompts for you and your client to discuss. The questions are written, but you can read them out loud to clients who cannot read.

Another way you can set up this game is to choose a song that your client likes (upbeat songs work best) and share your audio. In this case, you will need to have questions preselected, or have your client come up with questions. Sample questions are provided at the end of these instructions. Play the song for a period of time (depending on the child's age and developmental level, between 10 and 30 seconds), then pause the music and present a question. When the music is playing, dance with your client! Let yourself look silly.

Prompt: "Today, we are going to play a game called Dance Party. I am going to play some fun music, and we get to dance! You can dance whatever way you want to, and if you'd rather I not watch you dance, you can turn off the camera or move out of the camera's view. When the music stops, I'll ask a question, and we can both share our answers."

Sample Questions:

Feelings Questions

1. What's something that happened this week that made you laugh?
2. What's something that happened this week that made you feel sad?

3. What's something that happened this week that made you feel angry?

4. What's happened that happened this week that made you feel happy?

5. What brings your mood up when you feel upset?

6. How do you handle hard feelings?

7. What is something that relaxes you?

School Questions

1. What is your favorite thing about school?

2. What is your least favorite thing about school?

3. What is something your teacher does that helps you learn?

4. How is your school year going?

5. What is one thing you would change about school if you could?

Self-Esteem Questions

1. What is a challenge you overcame this week?

2. What is one thing you like about yourself?

3. What is something you are good at?

4. What do other people like about you?

5. When is a time that you were brave?

6. What's a compliment you can give yourself?

Social Skills Questions

1. What makes someone a good friend?

2. What do you do for fun with your friends?

3. How do you help your friends when they are having a hard time?

4. What do you do when you and a friend disagree?

5. How are your friends different from you?

6. How do you show your friends that you care about them?

Miscellaneous Questions

1. What is your favorite food?

2. What is your favorite game?

3. If you could have a superpower, what power would you have and why?

4. What's a funny story you can share?

I Can Make My Heart Go Fast

Suggested Age Group: 4 to 12

Therapeutic Benefits: Body work, mindfulness, muscle relaxation

Telehealth Benefits: This activity helps kids become aware of how different things affect what is going on inside their bodies and teaches them that they can control how their body feels. It is both a body activity and a cognitive behavioral intervention that teaches them to be aware of their feelings and body sensations, as well as what can change these feelings.

Setup: Start this activity by taking a few big breaths with your client. This helps bring them into the moment for the activity. Show your client how to take their pulse on either their neck or their wrist, and set a timer for 10 seconds while they count their heartbeats. Younger kids might need a caregiver's help counting the beats. If the child has a fitness device, they can simply check their heart rate with this, but taking their own pulse can bring them more fully present with the activity.

Once the client has measured their resting heart rate, give them the choice to run in place or do jumping jacks for 30 seconds. Do the chosen activity with them and keep count using a stopwatch. Encourage them to move as fast as they can for the full time.

At the end of the 30 seconds, have your client check their pulse again. Notice that their heart rate is higher than it was before the activity. Ask the child how their body feels right now and what emotions they experience when their heart is going faster.

Cue your client to do a breathing or relaxation exercise with you. (You can use activities in the cognitive behavioral section of this workbook or any breathing activity that your client has found beneficial in the past.) After the relaxation exercise, have your client take their pulse again. Ask your client how their body feels now. You can use the following script or a variation if appropriate.

Prompt: "Notice how your body felt when your heart was going fast. Did you feel tense or maybe a little nervous? When are some other times that your body has felt that way? Notice how your body felt when you relaxed and took deep breaths. How did that change the emotion you were experiencing? You can change how your body feels by moving quickly or relaxing. You can control what happens in your body!"

Mirroring

Suggested Age Group: 3 to 12

Therapeutic Benefits: Mindfulness, body control, communication skills, social skills

Telehealth Benefits: This activity promotes awareness of what the other person is doing and encourages kids to pick up on nonverbal communication. You can use it to promote conversation with your client, or you can do the activity in silence to focus more on nonverbal cues, which offer a low-pressure form of interaction. Kids have a lot of fun with this activity, and it helps increase their comfort with the telehealth setting. For kids who are anxious about being seen on the video, this activity can help increase their comfort with video sessions. This activity is also helpful for kids who might wander off during their sessions because it pulls their focus to you on the screen.

Setup: Decide if you want the client to mirror you or if you will mirror your client first, or let your client choose. If the child is hesitant about the activity, it can put them at ease for you to lead first, but some enjoy being in charge.

If you are going to lead first, you can introduce the activity this way: "We are going to try something different today. I want you to watch what I'm doing and to copy my movements as closely as you can. Try to do exactly what I'm doing with my body and my face."

If the client is going to lead, tell them: "I'm going to watch what you do and copy you as closely as I can."

When you are leading, make big, exaggerated stretches and facial expressions. Make silly faces and have fun with the activity! When it is the client's turn to lead, tone down your movements a bit so that it does not appear that you are mocking them.

Muscle Relaxation

Suggested Age Group: 5 to 12

Therapeutic Benefits: Mindfulness and relaxation, body awareness, affective monitoring

Telehealth Benefits: This activity helps children calm their bodies, which improves their focus and engagement in the session. This is an easy activity to do together that engages the child's body while keeping them in the frame during a video session.

Setup: There are muscle relaxation tutorials on YouTube if you prefer to share the activity with your client this way. The benefit of the video, of course, is that you are doing the activity directly with the child rather than instructing the child to do the activity. In addition, the video might show the child a way to approach the activity that is different than what you might show them (more perspectives can be a good thing!). On the other hand, you can still do the activity with the child if you are reading the prompt, and if you are not sharing your screen to view a video, the child has a better view of you and how you are doing the activity with them.

It is helpful to have the child check in with their body before and after this activity. Ask them to identify what feeling or feelings they are having right now and how strong those feelings are on a scale from 1 (not at all) to 10 (the most intense they have ever felt in their life). Check in again after the activity to see what effect the muscle relaxation exercise had on how they are feeling.

Prompt: "We are going to pretend our muscles are sponges that are full of water, and we want to wring the water out. We will start with our feet. Squeeze those feet-sponges as tightly as you can so that all the water drains out of them. Try to squeeze tightly for five whole seconds, 1... 2... 3... 4... 5.

"Okay, now let's do our legs. Squeeze all the water out of your leg-sponges as tightly as you can, 1... 2... 3... 4... 5.

"Next let's do our stomach-sponges. Squeeze all the water out of your stomach, as hard as you can, 1... 2... 3... 4... 5, and now your back, as hard as you can, 1... 2... 3... 4... 5.

"Let's squeeze our arms and shoulders next, as tightly as we can, 1... 2... 3... 4... 5, and our necks, 1... 2... 3... 4... 5, and finally, squeeze your head and face as tightly as you can, making the weirdest face you can think of, and squeeze out your face-sponge.

"Now, release all those muscles and relax your body. Drop your arms to your sides, and let your head fall. Take a deep breath. How do you feel?"

Scavenger Hunt

Suggested Age Group: 5 and up

Therapeutic Benefits: Communication skills, exploration of emotions

Telehealth Benefits: Though you lose the ability to read a certain amount of body language with telehealth, the flip side is the information you get about the client's living space. Seeing a client in their home environment, you learn invaluable information about where the client lives and who they are outside of your office. This activity is one that is not possible in the same way in your office—you could certainly have clients bring something from home for your session, but with the telehealth Scavenger Hunt, you can explore the client's response to the activity in real time as they choose which items fit with each prompt.

Setup: Tell your client that you want to learn more about them with this activity. Let them know that the point of the activity is to get to know them in a fun way.

Prompt: There are infinite prompts you can use for this activity, but it is not a good activity for bringing up traumatic or upsetting memories. Try to avoid prompts related to these topics; the goal is for your client to engage and have fun with the activity.

Feelings Prompts:

1. What's something that makes you happy?
2. What's something from the last time you took a trip?
3. What's something that was a gift from someone you love?
4. What's something you made?
5. What's something you are proud of?
6. What's something that reminds you of your _____ (someone close to them)?

Sensory Prompts:

1. Find something soft.
2. Find something with a bumpy texture.
3. Find something that tastes good to you.
4. Find something that is your favorite color.
5. Find something that makes you feel very comfortable.

Shake Out the Wiggles

Suggested Age Group: 3 to 10

Therapeutic Benefits: Body work, impulse control, centering

Telehealth Benefits: This can be a great activity if a young kid is "getting the wiggles" in their session. It can get them moving while keeping them engaged in the session. I often use this as a way to gently redirect a child when I notice they are having trouble focusing. It cues them back to the moment in a nonpunitive and fun way.

Setup: It helps to do this activity with the client in case they get self-conscious. Plus, you can model how moving around helps with regulation. Make sure that you keep yourself in the frame while doing your wiggles!

Prompt: "I think we need to get some wiggles out! Let's get up and move around a bit. Let's stand up and do a big stretch! Put your hands up way over your head and stretch your back out. Now, let's shake our hands out! And our arms, our heads, our bodies! Shake whatever feels comfortable for you, and keep going for 10 seconds. 1... 2... 3... 4... 5... 6... 7... 8... 9... 10! We did it!

"Okay, now that we've got all those wiggles shaken out, let's do another big stretch, from our feet all the way up to the tops of our heads. How do you feel? Are all the wiggles out of your body?"

If the client says yes, you can invite them to sit down and move on to a game or another intervention. If they say no, prompt them to spend another 10 seconds shaking out those wiggles! Repeat as needed.

Simon Says

Suggested Age Group: 5 to 12

Therapeutic Benefits: Mindfulness, body control, communication skills, social skills, listening, focus

Telehealth Benefits: Simon Says teaches listening skills, and you have to pay particular attention to whether the instruction started with the right prompt. It's a great way to build these skills while getting kids moving.

Simon Says is similar to the Mirroring activity, with an emphasis on verbal communication rather than nonverbal communication. It gets you moving but helps prompt the child to stay in the frame where you can see them. Kids who have a need for control particularly enjoy this game because the therapist has to do what the child tells them to.

Setup: Introduce the game to your client. Most kids are familiar with Simon Says, but you can easily explain the directions. Determine who will be Simon first (most kids want to go first, but some are uncertain about choosing commands, so they might ask you to start).

Prompt:

Simon says...

1. Put your hands on your head.

2. Jump up and down.

3. Open your mouth wide.

4. Close your eyes.

5. Turn in a circle.

6. Touch your nose.

7. Stand up.

8. Laugh out loud.

9. Make an angry face.

Wake Up Your Face Muscles!

Suggested Age Group: 3 to 10

Therapeutic Benefits: Emotion exploration and identification, body work, communication skills

Telehealth Benefits: Because the focus of this activity is facial muscles, it gets you and your client moving—with your bodies engaged—without bringing either of you out of the frame. You can get a good view of the faces the child is making.

Setup: You can simply search for "face muscle exercises for kids" or "kids face yoga" on YouTube to get tutorials that walk you and your client through this activity together. This presents a trade-off: By using a video, you and the client are following the instructions together instead of the client listening to your directions, but watching the video means that each of your faces is smaller on the screen. You can decide what is the best fit in each situation. I have found that kids who are more oppositional tend to do better with the videos because I am coming alongside them in the activity rather than leading it, but kids who are working on attachment prefer to do the activity in a way that lets them see my face best.

You can cue the child to check in with their emotions before and after this task to see how the activity affects how they are feeling in the moment.

Prompt: If you are not using a video, here is a suggested script to follow:

"Let's get the muscles in our faces moving! We talk about moving our bodies, but we don't always think about what that looks like in our faces. First, let's move our lower jaws back and forth—how does that feel? Do you feel your mouth relaxing a little bit? Now move it forward and backward and then let it hang down.

"Now, let's open our mouths as wide as they will go, like we are yawning the biggest yawn ever! Stick your tongue out as far as it will go and hold it out. Now close your mouth and puff as much air into your cheeks as you can! When they're full, try to push even more air in. Let me see how big you can make your cheeks!

"Now make a tiny hole between your lips and blow that air out of your mouth like you're blowing up a huge balloon. How does it feel when the air comes out of your mouth? When you're all out of air, scrunch your face up as tightly as you can. Bring your eyebrows down and make a squished face. Do you feel your muscles all pulling together?

"Now open your face up as far as you can! Raise your eyebrows, open your eyes wide, and open your mouth as far as you can, like you're about to yell. Now relax completely, and even let your head hang down if you want. Shake your head gently from side to side. Good job!"

Everyone's sensory experience is unique; that is why ink blot tests yield such a variety of responses. That being said, certain things tend to be consistent: Most people like soft blankets and have some kind of sweet tooth. However, neurodivergent kids tend to have unique sensory needs. For example, many autistic people cannot tolerate certain fabrics or types of clothing.

Although most child therapists have sensory items that kids can use during in-person sessions, it has been challenging to find sensory items and activities that can be done over telehealth. Kids can always bring their own sensory items into their telehealth sessions, but if a child does not own these items, this might not be an option. Additionally, some sensory activities (like making slime) that many therapists offer in their in-person offices might not work over telehealth. For example, clients might not have the supplies at home, caregivers might be concerned about making a mess, and young kids might need hands-on assistance for this kind of activity.

Although virtual sensory items are definitely not the same as in-person sensory activities, they can still be used effectively in therapy. This section contains 14 sensory activities that can be done via telehealth. Due to the nature of sensory work, some of the interventions listed here require that the client have certain things on hand; however, I have made an effort to keep any expense this would place on clients and their families to a minimum.

Antistress Game

Suggested Age Group: 5 and up

Therapeutic Benefits: Mindfulness and relaxation, exploration of emotions, coping skills

Telehealth Benefits: Antistress gives you several fidget and sensory options to explore. Although the sensory experience is not the same online as it is in person, playing around with the options on this app can give kids a sense of which items they prefer, and they can try out different coping skills before their caregivers invest in a specific one. In my in-person office, I like to keep a variety of sensory items that clients can try, and this is the closest you can get in a telehealth setting to letting clients try out different items.

Setup: Antistress is an app, so to get the most out of this intervention, your client should use a smartphone or tablet. If you are using an Android device or an iPad, the Jindoblu version of Antistress is free to download. There is also a paid version with more activities, but you can temporarily unlock those activities in the free version by watching an advertisement. (And, incidentally, watching the advertisement is a lesson in patience!) On an iPhone, Content Arcade Games has a version of Antistress that is free to download. There is significant overlap between the activities available on both apps.

Have the client download the version of the app that is compatible with their device, then share their screen and open the app.

Setup: Have the client explore the various activities in the app. Options include virtual fidgets and bubble wrap, as well as satisfying activities like mowing a lawn or cutting kinetic sand. Explore with the client how the various activities make them feel and what relaxes them.

Fidgets

Suggested Age Group: 3 and up

Therapeutic Benefits: Mindfulness and relaxation, coping skills

Telehealth Benefits: Most therapists keep various fidget items in their offices for clients to explore and use during their sessions. In many cases, clients will fidget without thinking about it or focusing on the fidget behavior. The fidgeting becomes a way to self-regulate while they focus on something else in the session.

In telehealth, incorporating a virtual fidget consumes more attention and focus. Therefore, you are in a position to draw their attention to the effect that the activity has on them and to encourage mindfulness and attention to the activity itself.

Setup: There are many options for online fidgets; simply putting "virtual fidget" into a search engine yields thousands of results. For the most part, you select the site you want to use, share your screen, and grant the client remote control of the screen. Some sites that I have used include:

1. *Fidget spinner:* https://ffffidget.com/

2. *Fidget cube:* https://scratch.mit.edu/projects/168946247/

3. *Bubble wrap:* https://scratch.mit.edu/projects/66060262/

4. *Pop it:* https://scratch.mit.edu/projects/531608427/

Prompt: "As you use the fidgets, pay attention to how you feel. How is the fidget affecting the feelings you're experiencing right now? When you're using the fidget, what happens in your body? Which fidgets help you feel relaxed?"

Fireworks

Suggested Age Group: 3 and up

Therapeutic Benefits: Mindfulness and relaxation, exploration of emotions

Telehealth Benefits: Obviously, real fireworks are not a safe option for in-person therapy sessions. Fire and small children do not go together. However, virtual fireworks are a fun and safe mindfulness activity.

Setup: Go to https://mocomi.com/freaky-fireworks/, share your screen, and grant the client remote control. They can choose which kinds of fireworks they want to use to create their own virtual fireworks show! Other apps and websites have similar games.

Prompt: "This is a fireworks game. You get to create your own fireworks show! Play around with the different fireworks to make your own celebration. Watch closely as the fireworks explode on the screen, and notice the colors and shapes created as you set off the fireworks."

Afterward, you can prompt the client to close their eyes and remember the images created by the fireworks. Ask them to imagine the fireworks in their mind, and let them know that they can return to this activity in their mind any time they feel stressed out, angry, or sad.

Mindful Hearing

Suggested Age Group: 6 and up

Therapeutic Benefits: Mindfulness and relaxation, exploration of emotions, listening

Telehealth Benefits: Mindfulness activities help kids relax and slow down. If a child is having trouble staying engaged in the session or staying in the frame, a mindfulness activity can help bring them back to the moment.

Setup: Many mindful listening activities are available online. For example, Annaka Harris has a mindful hearing activity on her website: https://annakaharris.com/mindful-hearing/. You can share audio and listen to the meditation together. As with other meditation activities, the benefit of doing a prerecorded lesson together is that you can model mindfulness to the client, and you take yourself out of the role of director of the activity. At the same time, though, some kids do better with the therapist prompting them to do the activity.

A suggested script is included here. As with all scripted activities, you can tailor the wording based on your client's individual needs, treatment goals, and background. If you have a bell in your home, use it for this activity. Otherwise, there are several free apps available, such as Mindfulness Bell.

Prompt: "We are going to sit quietly for a few minutes and see how many things we can hear. Take a moment to get comfortable in your seat, place your hands on your legs, and close your eyes if you want to. Take a couple of deep breaths: in, 1... 2... 3, and out, 1... 2... 3... 4... 5.

"Take a few moments to try to hear as many things you can in the room around you. Do you hear birds or wind outside? Traffic? Other people moving around inside your house? We are going to sit quietly for about ten seconds and see how much you can hear. [*Pause for ten seconds.*] Notice how many things you could not hear when we first started that you notice now.

"I am going to ring a bell, and I want you to try to see how long you can hear the ringing. Count slowly when you hear the chime, and see how high you can count before you stop hearing the bell. [*Play the chime.*] How high did you count? Now let's try it again, and see if you can listen even more closely and count even higher. [*Play the chime again.*]

"Now, open your eyes. What kinds of things did you notice when you stopped to pay attention to everything you could hear around you? How did you feel when you stopped to really, closely listen to the world around you?

"You can take a moment to try to listen to the sounds around you any time you are having trouble!"

Mindful Seeing

Suggested Age Group: 6 and up

Therapeutic Benefits: Mindfulness and relaxation, exploration of emotions, attention

Telehealth Benefits: All sensory-based mindfulness activities can help bring clients into the moment and redirect their focus to the session. If a child is having trouble being still or staying engaged, a quick mindfulness activity can help them regulate and re-center.

Setup: Annaka Harris has some excellent mindful seeing activities for kids on her website, https://annakaharris.com/mindful-seeing/, one of which involves using a focus rock. You can bring a rock to the session, and your client can easily find a rock outside to use for this activity.

If you are using the script below, find an aesthetically pleasing image using a search engine. Choose an image with colors or content that your client likes to help them engage with this activity. If you would like, you could show the client a couple of images and let them choose which one they would prefer to focus on. Share your screen with the client so you can both look at the image.

Prompt: "Take a moment to get comfortable, and close your eyes if you would like. Let's start by taking a few big breaths together. In... and out... in... and out... in... and out...

"Now open your eyes. Take a moment to look at the picture. What do you see? What shapes or figures are there? What colors do you see? Try to count as many different colors as you can identify.

"Now that you have been looking at the picture for a little bit, see if you can look even more closely. What kinds of things do you notice now that you did not notice when you first started looking? Are there colors you might not have noticed right away?

"Think about other times you might have noticed something after looking for a while that you didn't see right away. What did you learn, and how did you get yourself to take some time to look more closely?

"What about you? What things do people not notice about you right away, that they need to take a moment and look closer?

"Look at the picture again. Is there anything you notice now that you didn't see when you were looking before? Can you think of another time you looked at something this closely and noticed this many different details about it?

"Let's take a few more deep breaths together. In... and out... in... and out... Now let's stretch our hands over our heads, stretch our backs, and relax.

"Any time you are having trouble, you can choose something around you to focus on and look very closely at, noticing all of its unique details."

Mindful Smelling

Suggested Age Group: 6 and up

Therapeutic Benefits: Mindfulness and relaxation, exploration of emotions, memory work

Telehealth Benefits: As with the other sensory activities presented in this section, this can help the child self-regulate and attend to the session. Mindfulness activities are excellent for redirecting in a gentle and nonpunitive way.

Setup: There are two options for mindful smelling: You can have the child focus on what smells they can identify in their home, or if the client has something with a strong scent available, you can have the caregiver assist the child in using it. Essential oils (e.g., lavender, sandalwood, ylang-ylang) or cooking extract (e.g., vanilla, peppermint) work well for this.

Prompt: "Something a lot of people don't spend a lot of time thinking about is smells. We are surrounded by smells all day, but we don't always notice them the way we notice things we see or hear. Right now, I want us to take a moment to pay attention to what we can smell. Before we start, I want to let you know that a lot of smells are closely tied to memories. While we do this activity, notice any memories that come up for you. It is okay to let these memories go by, and it's okay to have feelings about these memories. Please let me know if you need to take a break or stop."

If the client is using a specific scent: "What do you have to smell today? What made you choose that one? Now I want you to close your eyes and take a breath through your nose, inhaling the smell. Notice what happens in your body as you sniff. Do your muscles relax? Do you get any feelings in your stomach or your chest? Notice what is happening on the inside when you experience this smell.

"Do any memories come into your mind? What does this smell remind you of? Remember, it's okay to let memories go by or to think about them more if you would like. Now open your eyes. How do you feel?"

If the client is identifying scents around them: "Close your eyes. We are going to take a few deep breaths, in through the nose and out through the mouth. I will count to five to breathe in and seven to breathe out. Breathe in, 1... 2... 3... 4... 5, and hold—now breathe out, 1... 2... 3... 4... 5... 6... 7. Let's do that again. Breathe in, 1... 2... 3... 4... 5, and hold—now breathe out, 1... 2... 3... 4... 5... 6... 7. Breathe in, 1... 2... 3... 4... 5, and hold—now breathe out, 1... 2... 3... 4... 5... 6... 7.

"Start to notice what you smell. Maybe you smell food, cleaning products, lotion, or perfume. As we breathe, see how many different smells you can notice.

"Now open your eyes. How do you feel?"

Mindful Tasting

Suggested Age Group: 10 and up

Therapeutic Benefits: Mindfulness and relaxation, exploration of emotions

Telehealth Benefits: I often had clients come to their sessions directly from school or other activities. Sometimes, sessions were right before snack time or even dinner. I encouraged caregivers to send their kids to sessions with snacks to avoid hunger crankiness in my office. Some kids who brought snacks to my office would want to share their food with me. This often helped build rapport.

When I switched to telehealth, some of the kids who previously shared snacks with me still wanted to share snacks as part of our sessions. Since they could not share their own food with me over telehealth, I would keep popcorn at my desk so I could join them in having a snack.

Mindful tasting helps kids come into the present moment and establishes rapport through the shared activity of having a snack together.

Setup: The child will need some kind of food or snack item in their home, which means that their caregiver must provide the food. For low-income families in particular, snack options might be limited. However, you can do this activity with literally any food (though preferably a food that the child likes), so this activity can work for most clients.

Some kids might have difficulty waiting until you prompt them to taste the snack, so this activity is most effective with kids who have the impulse control to wait until you tell them to eat the snack.

Prompt: "What snack did you bring today? Yum, that sounds tasty! Today I want us to try something: I want you to really, fully experience tasting that snack. Do you think we can try that? Okay, let's take one piece, and before you take a bite, smell it. What do you smell? Do you notice anything you haven't noticed before?

"Now place it on your tongue, and really pay attention to how it feels. What flavors are there? What texture? Now bite into it and notice how that feels. How does it taste? When you're ready, you can swallow your bite.

"How did it feel to really take your time and experience the taste of your snack? What did you notice that you didn't before? And what flavors did you taste?"

Mindful Touch

Suggested Age Group: 6 and up

Therapeutic Benefits: Mindfulness and relaxation, exploration of emotions, emotion regulation

Telehealth Benefits: This activity can help the child center themselves and bring down big emotions. It can also help kids who are having trouble due to hyperactivity calm down and stay present for the telehealth session.

Setup: Have either your client or the client's caregiver find something very soft in their home. It can be a fuzzy blanket, a stuffed animal, velvety fabric on a pillow or piece of clothing, or something similar. If you know you want to use this intervention prior to the session, have the caregiver set the client up with their soft item at the start of the appointment.

Prompt: "Do you like soft things? Me too! Today we are going to take a few minutes to pay very close attention to what something feels like. Do you have something soft with you right now? What is it?

"I want you to hold this soft item in your hands and take a second to really pay attention to what it feels like on your skin. What is it like to just be aware of the softness? Run your hands over it and see how it feels moving against your skin. You can put it against your face if you want to. Take a few deep breaths and just feel the soft texture on your skin. Breathe in, 1... 2... 3... 4... 5, hold, and breathe out, 1... 2... 3... 4... 5... 6... 7.

"Can you remember a time you paid such close attention to how something felt?"

Questions:

1. What was it like paying such close attention to the texture of something?
2. Did you like the soft texture? Is there another texture you like better?
3. Is there something you own that feels really good to hold in your hand?

If the child likes a particular texture and has a small item that feels good to them, you can discuss the option of them carrying this comfort item in their pocket so they can engage in mindful touch any time they are having trouble.

Perception:
What Color Do You See?

Suggested Age Group: 5 and up

Therapeutic Benefits: Attention, communication skills, understanding different perspectives

Telehealth Benefits: This activity helps kids understand that two people might have different perspectives on something, and that is okay. It helps them notice what they see when they look at something and accept that someone might disagree with them. Doing this activity over telehealth, you and your client are more likely to perceive different colors because your devices will have different settings (brightness, contrast, etc.).

Setup: The easiest way to set up this activity is to use Paint. You can go to "edit colors" and input the RGB numbers listed below. Use the bucket feature to fill the screen with that color. Ask the client which color they see, and share what it looks like to you. These colors are selected specifically because they are ambiguous—it is possible to see different colors when you look at them.

Colors:

1. Blue or green? R ≈ 2; G = 123; B = 118

2. Purple or blue? R = 116; G = 35; B = 245

3. Green or gray? R = 77; G = 93; B = 83

4. Red or pink? R = 224; G = 62; B = 83

5. Pink or purple? R = 141; G = 0; B = 115

Questions:

1. Were there any colors we saw differently that surprised you?

2. Was it ever hard to decide which color you were seeing?

3. How did it feel when we disagreed?

4. Is it possible we were both right about the colors?

Rubik's Cube

Suggested Age Group: 3 and up

Therapeutic Benefits: Focus, problem solving, executive functioning, asking for help, communication skills

Telehealth Benefits: I keep a Rubik's cube in my in-person office, and some kids enjoy trying to solve it. Sometimes, they become frustrated with the task and ask me to solve it for them. I can only solve one side at a time, which sometimes frustrates them but also normalizes that adults can be imperfect or make mistakes.

With the telehealth Rubik's cube, the client and I can work on the puzzle simultaneously. The website uses keyboard commands, so even with screen sharing, we can both be controlling and manipulating the cube simultaneously. There is also a "solve" function that is great for kids who have trouble leaving a task unfinished—that is something that was not an option in my in-person sessions!

Setup: Go to https://rubikscu.be/, share your screen, and grant remote control to the client. You can scramble the cube with the click of a button and manipulate it with your mouse or the F, R, U, B, L, and D keys. Ask your client if they want to work on the task together or independently.

In addition to the virtual cube, the site has tips and tutorials for how to solve a Rubik's cube, so if the client wants to learn how to solve it, you can learn this skill together.

Additional Notes: Rubik's cubes are a more complex fidget item, as there is a correct answer and a way to solve the fidget, whereas things like fidget spinners and cubes are simply meant to be manipulated. This adds a component of focus and problem solving to the task and makes this intervention more complex than standard fidgets. Kids seem to enjoy the option of working with me to solve the problem rather than one or the other of us working on it at a time, and that added layer of cooperation has been great for rapport building in my sessions.

Sand Tray: Free Play

Suggested Age Group: 3 and up

Therapeutic Benefits: Mindfulness and relaxation, communication skills, exploration of emotions

Telehealth Benefits: Sand work can be a fantastic therapeutic tool, but it is also such a mess! It is impossible to sanitize sand, making these in-person interventions more challenging in a post-pandemic world. The sensory component of sand tray work changes when you transition to telehealth, but the components of self-expression and exploration are still there.

In addition to reduced mess and concerns about germs, the virtual sand tray has all of the recommended pieces found in a traditional sand tray, but the child can add multiples of the same piece if they want to and alter the size. For example, if you have only one unicorn figurine in your office, the client is limited to one unicorn in their sand tray. With the telehealth version, they can have as many unicorns as they desire, in a variety of sizes. And can you ever have enough unicorns?

Setup: Go to https://onlinesandtray.com/. Share your screen, and grant the client remote control. (You can also have the client navigate to the website and share their screen with you.) From here, they will see seven categories of images:

1. Fantasy/mythical

2. Animals

3. Humans

4. Water

5. War and medical

6. Industrial (cars, buildings, bridges, etc.)

7. Nature

The first time I use this intervention, I like to use a nondirective approach. This allows the child to become comfortable with the task, and it gives me invaluable information about how they approach the sand tray. I narrate the child's choices and any emotions I see as they engage with the task.

Prompt: "This is called a sand tray. You might have used something like this in person before, but this is one that we can use in our telehealth session. There are a lot of different options for how to set up your sand tray, and you can use whatever pieces you would like. There is no wrong way to do the sand tray. There are many different images you can put in the tray, and you can make them bigger or smaller and position them any way you would like. Go ahead!"

Slime

Suggested Age Group: 3 and up

Therapeutic Benefits: Mindfulness and relaxation, body awareness, exploration of emotions

Telehealth Benefits: Like sand trays, slime tends to be very messy and difficult to do in an in-person office due to the materials and cleanup required. Caregivers might be willing to have children make slime as part of their telehealth sessions, but younger kids, especially, would require hands-on supervision while doing this activity. Although the sensory component of the activity changes with telehealth, there are some websites that allow you to create virtual slime. You can also use a mindfulness activity to imagine how the slime would feel if it were real.

Setup: There are two websites that I have used for this activity, and both have the same setup. Pull up the website, click "play," share your screen, and grant the client remote control. The first option, Slime Maker, involves simpler point-and-click play, which is good for younger kids or those using tablets for their sessions. The second option, My Slime Mixer, lets you play with the virtual slime once you finish making it by stepping on it with a shoe, hitting it with a fist, or pressing it with a waffle pattern. Of course, kids enjoy that option. Both websites let you customize the slime with colors and decorations.

1. *Slime Maker:* https://poki.com/en/g/slimemaker

2. *My Slime Mixer:* https://www.girlsgogames.com/game/my-slime-mixer

If your client is on a tablet or smartphone, there is a free app called Super Slime Simulator that has high-quality graphics that make the slime seem even more realistic. They can share their screen with you and choose from dozens of types of slime, colors, and mix-ins.

Prompt: "I know it's different making slime this way than in real life, but we can still pretend! Imagine you are mixing all the ingredients together with your hands. Feel them squishing between your fingers and on your skin. What does it feel like? Is it sticking? Keep imagining you are mixing it together, and when everything is all blended, stretch that slime as far as it will go. What does it look like all stretched out like that? How does it feel? If you mixed anything in your slime, do you feel it crunching or squishing in your hands?

"There might be times when playing with slime helps you, like when you feel nervous or when you are trying to calm down when you are angry. Sometimes, you might want the option to play with slime when you don't have any real slime available. But guess what? You can squish your imaginary slime any time you want to! Just picture it in your head and imagine it on your hands like you did just now."

Zen Rock Garden

Suggested Age Group: 3 and up

Therapeutic Benefits: Mindfulness and relaxation, exploration of emotions, creativity

Telehealth Benefits: I know some therapists who keep sand gardens in their offices for clients to use either as a mindfulness activity or as a fidget while talking during their session. As a therapist who works with many young children, it was not feasible for me to keep one, since I would have to vacuum between every single session when sand wound up on the floor. With telehealth, this is not something I have to worry about. Plus, with the activity on a screen, kids who might not have the motor skills to manipulate the tiny rake can still use the garden.

Another benefit of the virtual garden is that clients can add features, like rocks and grass, and customize the garden to their exact preferences. With a real Zen garden, they are limited to whatever items you have on hand.

Setup: Go to https://scratch.mit.edu/projects/39009 and share your screen with the client. Grant the client remote control. They can choose to rake the sand, smooth it, and add rocks or grass. The arrow keys change the size of the item, and the space bar changes the appearance.

Prompt: "Do you know what a Zen garden is? It's also known as a dry landscape garden, and it's a small patch of sand with different things like rocks and plants. People rake Zen gardens to feel in touch with nature and to just be present in the moment. Even though we can't have real sand, rocks, or plants on telehealth, I have something similar. I'm going to share with you a virtual Zen garden. That means it's on the computer. You can add rocks or plants if you want, and you can rake and smooth the sand. There is no right or wrong way to use this; I just want you to be in this moment."

Questions:

1. How did you feel when you were raking the garden?

2. What features did you decide to add, and how did you choose them?

3. What thoughts went through your mind as you did this activity?

4. If the garden you made was real and you could go sit in it, would you? What would you do there?

Zen Photon Garden

Suggested Age Group: 3 and up

Therapeutic Benefits: Mindfulness and relaxation, exploration of emotions, creativity

Telehealth Benefits: This activity is a more abstract variation on the Zen rock garden. Clients "rake" through light rather than sand and create various shapes and beams of light. This is a great mindfulness activity, and although there are similar exercises, the photon garden is not something I have been able to specifically replicate for in-person sessions. One fun thing about telehealth is finding these kinds of activities that were not an option before!

Setup: Go to https://zenphoton.com/, share your screen, and grant the client remote control. The client can decide how much they want to balance the diffuse, reflective, and transmissive settings to change how the light appears on their screen. Then they interact with the light by drawing lines on the image. They can save their results if desired.

Prompt: "Do you see this light? You can change its shape and what it is pointing at by drawing lines, like this. There isn't a right or wrong way to do this activity; you can just be in the moment and make the light look any way you want it to."

Questions:

1. How did this activity make you feel?

2. What kind of thoughts went through your mind as you were doing this?

3. When you look at the image now, what do you see?

4. Was there anything you were trying to make it look like as you did the activity? What?

After the activity, you can prompt the client to close their eyes and picture the light again in their mind. They can do this activity by imagining drawing lines on the light and use this as a coping skill any time they are having trouble.

Although we know children do not necessarily need to "talk through" things in order for therapy to be beneficial, middle and high school clients might need some support to feel comfortable talking. Depending on your theoretical orientation, you might also want to encourage children to process traumatic events or problem behaviors through talk. Not to mention, if you want to work on communication skills and appropriate emotional expression, you will have to incorporate talk into your sessions!

Talk and therapy are inseparable concepts, so it can be helpful to have ideas in your therapist toolbox that encourage clients to engage with you using words. The 12 activities detailed in this section help clients get comfortable expressing themselves verbally. Each one encourages clients to engage with you by talking, and many can be used in the same way whether you are seeing someone in person or over telehealth. Some require a certain amount of self-disclosure on the therapist's part, so be mindful of your boundaries with this when selecting your interventions.

Of course, some self-disclosure can build rapport and help clients feel comfortable engaging with you, but you want to be mindful of balancing what is helpful to share with the client and what might be inappropriate. I like to ask myself, "Am I sharing this information for myself or to help my client?" This is a good litmus test for what sharing will be helpful to the therapeutic process.

Alphabet Game

Suggested Age Group: 6 and up

Therapeutic Benefits: Communication skills, focus, cognitive challenging, cognitive flexibility

Telehealth Benefits: This activity lets kids get creative and think differently. It also does not involve talking directly about the client's presenting problem (despite having therapeutic benefits), so kids find it nonthreatening and are often more willing to engage if they are hesitant to talk directly about their treatment goals or things they are having trouble with. This can be a good starting point for building rapport or a gateway to talking about other concerns.

Setup: Prompt the client to choose a category. I always let the client choose a category first unless they specifically request that I start us off instead. (If the client prefers that you choose first, I recommend starting with a nonthreatening category like "types of desserts.")

You can use a word processor to make a document with every letter of the alphabet, one on each line. Add the name of the category at the top, and take turns with your client choosing a word for each letter. For example, if the client wants to do the category "animals," they could say, "A for alligator," and you could say, "B for bunny," and so on.

Some letters (such as J, Q, and X) are more challenging than others. Whoever gets these letters might have to think very hard to come up with ideas, and this opens you up to creativity. Is there a word that is not directly related to your category that might fit? Is there an alternate spelling you can use? As the game gets challenging, you and your client might work together to come up with an answer for each letter.

Sample Categories:

Rapport Building:

- Animals

- Cities/towns

- Foods that you like

- Games

- Jobs

- Names

- Pets

- Superpowers

- Types of candy

- Vacation destinations

Therapeutic:

- Coping skills

- Emotions

- Things I do when I feel _____

- Things I do with friends

- Things that make me feel _____

Auto Complete Game

Suggested Age Group: 8 and up

Therapeutic Benefits: Communication skills, creativity, exploration of emotions

Telehealth Benefits: Unless your clients bring devices like tablets or phones into their in-person sessions, this is an activity that you would only use over telehealth. If a child is transitioning from in-person sessions to telehealth, it can be helpful to offer activities that were not an option for in-person sessions, since it makes the telehealth session different in a fun way. This is a fun game that usually makes clients laugh but also gets them talking about what the game brings up or reminds them of.

Setup: Your client needs to be on a device that has auto complete, like a tablet or smartphone. Ideally, have the child share their screen for this activity because then you will be able to see what they type in real time, whereas the chat feature will only show you the full story after they send the message.

Tell your client that you want to play a game where they write something using auto complete. Give them the first part of the sentence, and let them choose which auto complete option they want to finish it. This can lead to some pretty silly sentences, which is a lot of fun for the client, and you can discuss their choices in the game.

When the client types the first part of the sentence, auto complete offers three choices for how to continue. With each word the client chooses, they are given three options for the next word, and they can keep choosing words until they feel the sentence is complete. You can choose from the following sentence prompts or create your own.

Suggested Prompts:

- My mom is...
- My dad is...
- I am...
- I love...
- I hate...
- I am good at...
- I have trouble with...
- School is...

- My best friend is...
- Therapy is...
- I feel...
- My favorite thing is...
- The worst thing is...
- I need...
- I want...

Chats

Suggested Age Group: 8 and up

Therapeutic Benefits: Communication skills, exploration of emotions, social skills

Telehealth Benefits: Some clients do not want to talk in their sessions. While therapeutic silence is a valid intervention and often the most appropriate choice, sometimes a client wants to share but does not feel comfortable putting words to their feelings. When this happens, the chat feature can help lower their guard and let them be more forthcoming about what they want to be able to say. This is also helpful for clients who feel anxious about speaking or autistic clients who might become nonverbal when they feel significant stress.

Although you lose tone with chat messages compared to talking out loud, I have had several clients share things over chat that they had avoided saying out loud. Clients who tended to be quiet in sessions, once introduced to the chat feature, started sharing a lot in their sessions.

In a telehealth appointment, the chat feature can also let the client cue you if they have a privacy concern. They can type, "I think my (parent, sibling, etc.) is listening right now," making you aware of the concern without the client having to alert the person listening.

Setup: Let the client know where the chat feature is on your telehealth platform. You want to make sure they understand that they need to use the chat feature on your HIPAA-compliant platform and not the chat feature in any of the therapy games you may be using, since those chats are not encrypted. You can tell the client that they can use the chat to say anything they want.

Because chat means sacrificing some nonverbal communication, I do ask that clients who prefer to talk to me over chat leave their video on and stay in the frame so that I can see their body language while we talk over chat. This way, I can ensure that I am picking up on any nonverbal distress or big emotions that come up in the session.

There is no specific prompt or activity that you need to do; this intervention simply allows clients to communicate with you in a different way if that is more comfortable for them or a better fit for their needs.

Deck of Cards

Suggested Age Group: 6 and up

Therapeutic Benefits: Communication skills, exploration of emotions, exploration of coping skills

Telehealth Benefits: This is a fun way to get kids talking about different topics. You use a set of ready-made prompts to discuss a variety of topics, and you never know which topic will come up next. This is a great activity to pull out when clients feel that they have "nothing to talk about today."

Setup: If you or your client has a physical deck of cards handy, you can use them for this activity. If not, you can go to https://deck.of.cards/, click "shuffle," and choose the top card. You can screen share with your client and take turns with control to each choose your own cards. Another platform that works is https://playingcards.io/, using the Matching, Crazy Eights, or Go Fish rooms to access a virtual deck of cards.

This activity involves you and your client taking turns answering the questions, so you will have to engage in some self-disclosure. Self-disclosure can be an important tool in therapy, especially for building rapport with children, but we must remain mindful that we do so in the client's best interest. We must also remain mindful of our own triggers when we are sharing any personal information with clients.

Prompt: "I know sometimes it's hard to think of things to talk about, or something might be on your mind that you forget when it's time for us to meet. That's okay! I have a game we can play to give us ideas. We are going to take turns drawing cards, and we will answer whatever question comes with that card. I have a list of questions here."

The following is a set of question prompts for a standard deck of cards, but you are welcome to add, remove, or reword questions as you see fit and based on individual client needs and treatment goals.

Card Questions:

Joker: Wild card—choose your own question

Spades—Fun Questions:

A: Where would you go on vacation if you could go anywhere?

2: What is your favorite movie and why?

3: What is your favorite memory?

4: If you could make one rule that everyone had to follow, what would you choose and why?

5: What is your favorite type of music, and what do you like about it?

6: What is the best dream you have ever had?

7: If you could change your name, what name would you choose?

8: If you won the lottery, what would you do with the money?

9: If you could meet any famous person, whom would you meet and why?

10: If you could meet any historical figure, whom would you choose and why?

J: What is your favorite book?

Q: What is your favorite holiday and why?

K: What is your favorite season and why?

Clubs—Feelings Questions:

A: What is something that recently made you cry?

2: What is something that recently made you laugh?

3: What is something that recently made you angry?

4: What is something that recently made you scared?

5: What do you need most when you have big feelings?

6: When is a time that you felt guilty?

7: What is something that makes you feel happy?

8: When is a time that you felt embarrassed?

9: What does it feel like when someone tells you that you did something wrong?

10: Do you ever have a hard time sleeping? What do you do?

J: What do you do when you feel sick?

Q: How do you feel when you spend time alone?

K: Do you think you are an optimist or a pessimist? Why?

Diamonds—Social Skills Questions:

A: What's one nice thing about your best friend?

2: What makes someone a good friend?

3: What makes someone a bad friend?

4: How do you know if someone is a bad influence?

5: What do you think your friends think of you?

6: What do you wish your friends thought about you?

7: Have you ever had a friend lie to you? What happened?

8: If you could give a presentation on any topic, what would you choose and why?

9: How do you feel about nicknames?

10: In what ways do you try to be like your friends?

J: When do you tend to be very quiet?

Q: When do you tend to talk a lot?

K: What do you do when you need space?

Hearts—Self-Esteem Questions:

A: What is your favorite thing about your personality?

2: How do you usually feel about yourself?

3: When is a time you were proud of yourself?

4: What do you think you will be like in five years?

5: How do you fix mistakes?

6: What is a goal you hope to accomplish in the next year?

7: What do you do that helps your family?

8: What do you notice when you see yourself in photographs?

9: How are you different than you were a year ago?

10: If they had Olympic events in everything you can imagine, what would you get a gold medal for?

J: What things are important to you?

Q: Do you prefer to be a leader or a follower? Why?

K: What makes you feel special?

Meet Your Pets

Suggested Age Group: 3 and up

Therapeutic Benefits: Communication skills, social skills, building empathy, exploration of emotions, mindfulness

Telehealth Benefits: It took less than a day of telehealth for me to realize that the best part of meeting with clients in their homes is that I get to see everyone's pets, and many clients expressed excitement that seeing me in my home office meant that my cats might make an appearance on camera! Pets make great conversation starters; after all, who isn't excited to see an animal on a video call? The pet can assist in your session as a mindfulness tool, offering emotional support in real time.

Client Pets: If a client has a pet that they use for emotional support, I have them bring the pet to their session when we know we will be discussing a hard topic. They can de-escalate in real time by stroking the animal, and I have seen several cats and dogs cue clients to regulate and calm down when they were getting escalated.

Therapist Pets: Do you have pets at home? Bring them into your telehealth office! Children get excited to see my cats and even ask if the cats will join us for their sessions. I like to find commonalities between my clients and my pets, tying my pets' history into my client's treatment. This might take some creativity on your part. The following are some examples of how this works for me.

Vera, my long-haired cat, used to be a stray. She lived outside and was afraid a lot of the time, and even though she is now safe at my house, she still gets scared of things for seemingly no reason. If a child has trauma history, they can often relate to being triggered and not being able to articulate what is bothering them.

Armani, my tuxedo cat, has lived with me for almost his entire life. He is 11 years old now and has diabetes. Because of his diabetes, he has to get insulin shots twice per day. Armani does not like getting shots, and sometimes he grumbles when it is time for his medicine, but he tolerates it because he knows he feels better afterward. He helps me talk with kids about taking medication.

At one point, both Armani and Vera needed dental cleanings and had teeth extracted. As you can imagine, they were both less than thrilled about going to the vet, being put under anesthesia, and recovering from the procedure, but they both feel so much better. Sometimes, we have to do things that are no fun (or even uncomfortable) to keep ourselves healthy.

Think about your own pets—how might they fit into your sessions and benefit your clients?

Sentence Stories

Suggested Age Group: 8 and up

Therapeutic Benefits: Communication skills, social skills, teamwork, exploration of emotions

Telehealth Benefits: By sharing your screen, you and your client can see the story as it is written out. A fictional story can be less threatening to children, and themes that arise from the story can be tied back to the treatment plan.

Setup: Open a blank document in a word processor, and share your screen with the child. Type the story as you tell it. Before starting the activity, choose what you would like the story to be about, taking into consideration your client's interests, treatment goals, and background. As the story fleshes out, you can ask questions or narrate what the child shares with you as a way to prompt emotional exploration. In your first sentence, name a character who is similar to your client so that they can relate to the character.

Prompt: "Let's write a story together! We are going to take turns and make a story about _____. I will say a sentence, then you say a sentence, and we will keep going until we have an awesome story."

Story Ideas:

- Overcoming fear

- Handling anger

- A happy memory

- Two friends learning to get along

- Someone overcoming a challenge

- Someone learning a new skill

- A parent taking care of their child

Three Songs

Suggested Age Group: 6 and up

Therapeutic Benefits: Communication skills, identity work, exploration of emotions

Telehealth Benefits: This is a great way to get to know clients of all ages, but teenagers in particular engage by connecting over music. I ask clients about their music preferences all the time, and one added benefit of telehealth appointments is that you can share sound on your computer and not the video, keeping the emphasis on the lyrics.

Setup: There are so many different ways to incorporate music into sessions. Sometimes, I ask kids to tell me what song represents how they feel today, how their week has gone, or just a song that is on their mind today. This intervention is more in-depth, and you can do it in a session or ask them to come to the next session with their choices.

You can start by asking the client about their music tastes before getting to the specific prompt. Many respond positively when you share some of your music tastes as well, and you might find that you like some of the same bands!

Although most people have some musical preferences, you might occasionally encounter a child who does not like music. Whether they are simply saying this because they want to say no to whatever you suggest, or they truly have not found any music they enjoy, it is okay to transition to another intervention if this is not a good fit. They might also decide that they cannot narrow their response down to three songs; this is also perfectly fine!

Prompt: "I want you to think about the music you listen to. Now think about the person that you are now. You know how music can make you feel different ways, and music can represent different things for us. I'm wondering what songs speak to who you are. Can you think of three songs that represent you? Which songs would you choose?"

Questions: After they choose their three songs, listen to them together, one at a time. After each song, explore the client's connection to the song.

1. How do you feel when you hear this song?

2. What is your favorite lyric?

3. Think about the first time you heard this song. When was it? What was going on?

4. When do you like listening to this song the most?

5. How does this song represent you?

6. What made you choose this song for this activity?

Twenty Questions

Suggested Age Group: 5 and up

Therapeutic Benefits: Communication skills, exploration of emotions, critical thinking

Telehealth Benefits: This activity is simple and only requires you and the client to interact verbally, so it works with any type of device or telehealth platform. It is a fun way to help clients get more comfortable participating in sessions and answering questions that you ask.

Setup: Decide who will go first, you or your client. Whoever goes first chooses something, and the other person has 20 yes-or-no questions to guess what it is. If you have a game like Hedbanz, you can use the cards from the game to choose topics: When it is your turn to guess, hold a card up to the camera so your client can see it, and when it is the client's turn to guess, you can simply look at the card. That makes for a fun and simple guessing game with common words with which you and your client are likely both familiar.

Another option is to let this activity be open-ended, so your client can choose anything they want. Some kids have difficulty choosing, so this might be stressful for them— as with all therapeutic activities, this could either be an opportunity to work through that emotion or a chance to show the child that you will meet their needs when they are having a hard time. If you prompt your client to choose anything they can imagine, there is a good chance that they will pick something you have never heard of; this is an opportunity to model frustration tolerance and handling failure appropriately.

You can choose things that relate to the client's treatment as a way to get them talking about a specific skill. For example, you could choose an emotion for them to guess.

I find it helpful to provide a list of possible questions to the child so they have options if they are struggling to guess what I am thinking of.

Possible Questions:

1. Are you a living thing?

2. Are you fictional?

3. Are you some kind of story?

4. Are you something I could eat?

5. Are you larger than a refrigerator?

6. Are you human?

7. Are you something I could see?

8. Are you made by people?

9. Are you found in nature?

10. Do you move by yourself?

11. Did you exist 100 years ago?

12. Have we talked about you in therapy before?

13. Could I hold you in my hand?

14. Are you heavy?

15. Do you make noise?

16. Are you made from organic material?

17. Do people use you every day?

18. Are you a primary color?

19. Do you get very cold?

20. Would I find you at my house?

Virtual Vacations

Suggested Age Group: 5 and up

Therapeutic Benefits: Communication skills, creativity, exploration of emotions, visualization

Telehealth Benefits: Unless you use computers in your in-person sessions, this is an activity that you can only do over telehealth. This was very popular with my clients early in the COVID-19 pandemic, when their vacations got canceled, because we could do an online version of the vacation in their session! (Of course, it was nowhere near as good as a real vacation, but we work with what's available.) I also use this activity to help clients describe vacations they actually took—some kids have a hard time putting words to things, and the visualization aspect of this activity helps.

Setup: Launch Google Earth and share your screen. Ask the client for a vacation destination, and search for that location. You can ask the client to tell you where they actually went for a vacation, where they will go in the future, or even where they would go right now if they could go anywhere. Sometimes, I simply ask, "If we could have our session today anywhere in the world, where would you like us to be?" In addition to Earth, there is also Google Moon, which has a less interesting "street view" but can be fun as well.

Questions:

1. Have you ever been to this place in real life? Tell me about it.

2. What made you choose this location?

3. What would you do if we were at this place now?

4. Would you want to live in this place? Why or why not?

5. Whom would you bring on this vacation?

Vision Boards

Suggested Age Group: 10 and up

Therapeutic Benefits: Goal setting, exploration of emotions, identity work, creativity

Telehealth Benefits: Vision boards are a great way to help clients articulate goals creatively. This could be seen as an art project, but I like to have kids talk through the choices they make with their vision board to flesh out what their focus is and how their identity ties into what they see for themselves in their life.

In my office, I keep a rather large stack of old magazines for vision boards, but there are limits to this. Magazines are a finite resource, and you can only use an image once. It is impossible to have every type of magazine on hand, so a child's particular interests might not be reflected. Kids with fine motor skills issues might struggle to cut out the picture they want to use. Or a client might want to change something on the vision board but they have already glued it down. This can always be an opportunity to work through feelings or build frustration tolerance, but telehealth vision boards are easy to modify, so you can keep the focus on goal setting and identity work in the activity without other frustrations interfering.

With a virtual vision board, the client can use any image that they have or that can be found online (as long as the board is just being used for a session, you do not have to worry about copyrighted images). They can move images around and adjust sizes if they want to, and they can make changes to the board as many times as they want.

Setup: I use the website Canva for telehealth vision boards. There is a paid option, but I stick with the free version. Depending on the client's preferences, I either share my screen and grant the client remote control or have them share their screen as they create their vision board. You can prompt the client to think about something in their future, make a board that represents who they are, or have them create anything else you want to explore with them in session.

As the client works on their vision board, I narrate and query their image choices, asking questions like "What speaks to you about this image?" and "What does this image represent to you?" Afterward, I have them save their vision board as a reminder of their goals and how they see themselves. I also save a copy for their chart (another telehealth benefit is that both you and the client can have access to the "original" board) and sometimes bring it back a few months later to see how they would change the vision board based on how things have changed since they originally made it. Again, they can make those changes easily over telehealth!

Would You Rather

Suggested Age Group: 5 and up

Therapeutic Benefits: Communication skills, decision-making, critical thinking

Telehealth Benefits: This is an easy activity that only requires verbal engagement between you and your client. This game gets them thinking and talking, and they get to make a choice, helping with their sense of autonomy and control.

Setup: You can share the list of questions with the client by screen sharing, or you can simply explain the activity to them if you are making up prompts in the moment. I find clients are most comfortable and forthcoming with this activity if I start with "easy" (nonthreatening) questions, and then work into deeper topics. Optional prompts are included here, but you can use other prompts that you find online or that you and your client think of yourselves. You want to ensure you use developmentally appropriate questions for each client, and there is no limit to the topics you can discuss with Would You Rather.

In order for this activity to be most effective, you must also engage in some self-disclosure. Clients typically do not like for you to pose question after question without engaging yourself, so be mindful of what you are sharing when you do this activity. Self-disclosure can be for the client's benefit and build trust when appropriate.

Possible Questions:

1. Would you rather have cake or pie?

2. Would you rather stay up late or wake up early?

3. Would you rather have soda or flavored water?

4. Would you rather only have breakfast foods or only have desserts for the rest of your life?

5. Would you rather live on a beach or on a mountain?

6. Would you rather be able to get nutrients through the sun (photosynthesis) or be able to breathe underwater?

7. Would you rather have pizza or tacos?

8. Would you rather clean your room or wash dishes?

9. Would you rather get a pet cat or a pet dog?

10. Would you rather be able to learn a new language in a day or be able to play any sport really well?

11. Would you rather only need one hour of sleep per night or have a photographic memory?

12. Would you rather live in a space station or under the ground?

13. Would you rather be a bird or a fish?

14. Would you rather be able to predict the future or change the past?

15. Would you rather have every subject in school come easily to you or never have to go to school again?

16. Would you rather know you could never break a bone or know you could never get a paper cut?

17. Would you rather have everyone you met want to be your friend or everyone you talked to do whatever you say?

18. Would you rather have $20 right now or $100 in one month?

19. Would you rather have 100 friends you are not close with or one really close friend?

20. Would you rather be super strong or be able to fly?

21. Would you rather be really rich or have everyone like you?

22. Would you rather be powerful or smart?

23. Would you rather never be able to tell a lie or never be able to tell the truth?

24. Would you rather have no emotions or feel every emotion intensely, 10/10?

Your Story

Suggested Age Group: 8 and up

Therapeutic Benefits: Communication skills, exploration of emotions, narrative work, mindfulness, cognitive restructuring, identity work

Telehealth Benefits: Narrative work can be so healing for trauma survivors, and it can help clients notice underlying patterns, core beliefs, and cognitive distortions. Having a client tell their story can allow them to explore all of these themes in a safe environment.

Telehealth makes it easy to put a client's story together. This can be done in a myriad of ways, and you can tailor the prompt based on the client's background, the strength of your therapeutic rapport, and their current mental health needs. A great thing about video sessions is that you can share your screen and write down the client's story as they tell it, and they can see it written out as they share it. This allows you to process what they are sharing and their experience of sharing their story in real time. It is also very easy to save the story to continue at the next session.

Setup: As the child tells you their story, write down what they are saying. Depending on your typing speed, you might not be able to transcribe word-for-word, so you may want to use bullet-point notes instead. Whichever approach allows you to keep up with your client is best. Do not correct, interrupt, or ask questions. When they have finished their story, go back through it with them.

As you go through the story, do not question the client's memory or experience of events. You are instead looking at places where their internal beliefs might be mistaken. The approach is one of curiosity, not correction. For example, if the child describes abuse, it is invalidating to question the accuracy of their memory or the severity of the abuse, but it is helpful to query and offer correction if the client states that the abuse was their fault.

Prompt: "It's very important that you feel heard and that I listen to you. Do you know how we have been talking about ____? Well, today I want you to tell me your story about that, in your own words. I am going to write down what you say, and I'm going to share my screen so you can see what I'm writing. If I get something wrong, please tell me so I can fix it. After you finish telling me your story, we will talk about it together, but first I want to just listen to your perspective."

Questions:

1. *If you notice a cognitive distortion:* Is there another way we might think about this? Are we sure this is true? What's an alternative thought we might have here?

2. What did you notice as you talked about this memory? Is there anything you remembered that you hadn't thought of before?

3. What did you notice about your feelings as you shared this story?

4. What was it like seeing your story in writing as we went through it together?

One of the biggest challenges to adapting to telehealth with kids has been developing and implementing play interventions, particularly nondirective play. As we know, kids process their feelings through play and do not necessarily put this process into words. Nondirective play also gives kids a sense of control over their environment and agency in their therapy sessions, which is important for building rapport and in progressing toward their treatment goals.

The observational data you gather from giving your client this level of control over play and their session is invaluable, and the added graphics and sound effects that most of these interventions provide are so engaging for clients. As with in-person nondirective play, let the client tell you their names for different objects and how they want things to work in the game. There are some challenges with this—as we learned in the board games section of this book, many computerized activities have rules and limits coded in, but you can roll with these challenges and adapt the activities as needed.

This section includes 15 play activities that I use in my telehealth sessions, with instructions for setup for both you and your client. These interventions can be used with an observational approach (where the child is the primary actor in the game as you narrate their play and are physically present with them), or you can directly interact by joining in the play yourself. As with all things therapy, this will be based on your orientation and each client's needs.

Cars

Suggested Age Group: 5 and up

Therapeutic Benefits: Nondirective play, interactive play, competitive play, aggressive play

Telehealth Benefits: Kids love playing with matchbox cars in my in-person office, but the online version takes this activity to a new level. It's much easier to race each other when you are both cars on the screen and your bodies can't get in each other's way, and the cars get smashed up as you play. Plus, the game has some awesome sound effects that kids love.

Setup: Go to https://www.crazygames.com/game/madalin-cars-multiplayer and select "play now." When the loading screen finishes, click "play." Choose the car you'd like to play, then select "multiplayer." This will bring you to the list of available rooms.

To create a private room, put your player name (you can enter your real name or a nickname, or the game will automatically generate a random name for you) and a room name. Uncheck the box next to "create public room." Click "create room."

Have your client navigate to the game page, choose their player name, and then type in the room name *exactly* as you created it, as it is case sensitive. (Sometimes kids need help inputting the room name, but this becomes an opportunity to practice asking for help and overcoming a challenge.) Have them select "join room." Your client will spawn into the room you created, and the two of you can play without any other players joining your game.

Alternate Setup: Another way to play cars in your telehealth sessions is to use https://www.crazygames.com/game/crazy-stunt-cars-multiplayer. You can either pull the game up and share your screen or have your client pull it up and share their screen. Choose "play now" and then "single player." Let the client toggle through the choices to decide which car they want to be. Although this version does not allow you to create a private room where you are both present, the room has various terrains, and different cars handle differently (for example, the cars that go fastest on the road have a hard time driving over sand). This opens up conversation about priorities, strengths and weaknesses, and how some qualities can be a deficit in some contexts but helpful in others.

Dollhouse

Suggested Age Group: 3 and up

Therapeutic Benefits: Exploration of emotions, communication skills, exploration of relationship patterns

Telehealth Benefits: One of my favorite things about telehealth is that cleanup is minimal. You can present a game or activity, and no matter how the child approaches it, cleanup consists of refreshing the page or closing the window. No sanitizing, no organizing.

The figures and miniatures that clients can choose to put in the dollhouse are organized along the side of the screen, so clients can see all their options and find what they are looking for quickly. In addition, they can add multiples of the same piece and are not limited by the number of toys that you happen to have in your office. They can also manipulate the size of each piece, so if they are creating a scene of their family, you get more information about their perception of these relationships.

Setup: Go to https://onlinedollhouses.com/, share your screen, and grant the client remote control. You can prompt the client to set up the dollhouse to represent their own home, their ideal home, or a place they used to live. Or you can take a nondirective approach and let the client engage with the platform in whatever way they choose.

Questions:

Create Your Home:

1. How is your home different from the dollhouse you set up?

2. Where did you place each member of your family?

3. What is each family member doing?

4. Where in this house do you feel the safest?

Create Your Ideal Home:

1. Tell me about the home you created.

2. What things were important for you to include in this home?

3. Who lives here? What are they like?

4. How is this place different from your home?

5. How is this place the same as your home?

Create a Previous Home:

1. Where is this place?

2. When did you live here?

3. Tell me about what it was like living here.

4. Who lived here with you?

5. What did you like about this home? What did you dislike?

Free Play:

1. Who lives in this house?

2. Do the people get along with each other?

3. What happens in this house?

4. Is this a safe place to live?

Escape Rooms

Suggested Age Group: 8 and up

Therapeutic Benefits: Problem solving, asking for help, exploration of emotions, frustration tolerance

Telehealth Benefits: Escape rooms require strong problem-solving skills and perseverance in the face of frustrating tasks. There are hundreds of websites with different puzzles to choose from, so you can choose a room with a theme that fits your client's interests. If the client prefers to work independently, you can watch and narrate as they figure out solutions, or the two of you can work together to escape. I am not presently aware of a similar game that can be done in an in-person session.

Setup: There are many websites that have free escape room flash games. One that I have used is https://www.365escape.com/. (There are also several escape room games available on Roblox's platform.) Pull up the site, share your screen, and let the client select which escape room they want to solve. This particular site has genres like scary and adventure, so you can choose a room based on what will hold the client's attention. The game can get challenging, and choosing a theme that fits the client's interests makes it more likely that they will work through this frustration rather than wanting to discontinue the activity when it gets difficult.

If desired, you can give the client the option to search for walkthroughs to help them solve particularly difficult components of the escape room.

Questions:

1. What was your emotional experience with this activity?

2. What was it like for you when you had trouble finding the solution?

3. What was it like receiving my help when you had trouble?

4. What did you like about the escape room? What did you dislike?

5. If you were to create an escape room of your own, what would it look like?

Hatchimals

Suggested Age Group: 3 and up

Therapeutic Benefits: Attachment work, identity work, following directions, exploration of emotions, making choices

Telehealth Benefits: Hatchimals are a popular toy that a lot of kids love to collect and play with. You purchase an egg, and the Hatchimal inside is a surprise. This activity pulls from the child's interest in Hatchimals while getting them to engage in exploring their identity and emotions. The game itself is primarily based on commands that are not text-based, so clients do not need to be able to read to understand most of the game, but you can read them the text-based prompts as needed.

Setup: Go to https://kizi.com/games/hatchimals-maker, share your screen, and grant the client screen control. Click "play," then the play icon. The client is prompted to decide what their Hatchimal egg looks like. Next, they are prompted to care for the egg. The egg uses icons to communicate what it needs in order to grow and be ready to hatch, including warmth, rocking, touch, cleaning, and music. When the egg feels taken care of and ready, it rocks back and forth to indicate that it wants to hatch.

Before the egg hatches, the client will be prompted to take a quiz to determine what their Hatchimal's personality will be (its favorite food, where it wants to live, etc.). When the egg hatches, they can name it. The resulting Hatchimal will have a mood, a special talent, and a weakness, which can prompt discussion. When I have played this game, moods have included brave, sad, and shy; talents have included playing guitar, painting, and burping; and weaknesses have included bedtime, math, and newspapers. Some of the choices are a bit silly, but they can open up discussion about the client's feelings, talents, and difficulties.

Questions:

1. What do you have in common with your Hatchimal?

2. How are you different from your Hatchimal?

3. Are there ways that you wish you were more like your Hatchimal?

4. What would you change about your Hatchimal if you could?

Hide-and-Seek

Suggested Age Group: 10 and up

Therapeutic Benefits: Focus, problem solving, visualization

Telehealth Benefits: In-person hide-and-seek has an attachment emphasis, since clients go through the experience of finding and being found by the therapist. The telehealth version is not quite the same, since the party who is hiding does not fully disappear. However, this online version of hide-and-seek still requires executive-functioning skills to determine where the other party hid. The website uses a world map from Google Street View to allow you to hide anywhere on the planet. This offers significantly more options than what I have available in my office, and it opens up discussion about why the client chose their particular hiding place.

Setup: This is one of the few telehealth activities for which I have created an account to use the platform. In order to create a private room where just you and your client are present, you need to be logged in, and you can use a Gmail account to make this account. Go to https://hideandseek.world/, log in, choose what color you want to be, and click "play with friends." This creates a link that you can send to the client, and they can join you in your private room. The free version of the game limits how many rounds you can do per game, but you can create a new room to play more games.

Once you are both in the game room, you take turns "hiding" by choosing a location from the map. The seeker gets the Google Street View of the location and has to guess where in the world the hider is. Points are tallied based on how far from the hider's location you guess.

Questions:

1. What made you choose this location to hide?

2. Have you ever been to this place in real life?

3. If you have not been to this area, what do you think it is like there?

4. How did you decide on your guess about where I was hiding? What clues did you notice?

LEGO®

Suggested Age Group: 3 and up

Therapeutic Benefits: Creativity, mindfulness and relaxation, visual spatial skills

Telehealth Benefits: When you keep a box of LEGO® pieces in your office, no matter how thorough you are when you clean up between sessions, at some point you are going to step on a piece. With virtual LEGO®, this does not happen! No cleanup, no stray bricks to step on. Additionally, the virtual platform gives the client the option to customize the size, shape, and color of the bricks, giving them more control over the activity. They can create duplicates, and they do not have to spend time digging for the brick they are looking for.

Setup: Go to https://www.mecabricks.com/, share your screen, and grant the client remote control. There are sets to choose from, but any room you create has the option for the client to build in whatever way they choose.

You can prompt the client to build something specific, but I typically take a nondirective approach and see what the client decides to create. They can also decide to try to create a specific build from one of the many, many LEGO® sets provided on the website.

Mecabricks also has an option to export a build in progress, so clients can leave unfinished pieces on your hard drive, and you can import this at the next session for the client to continue building. Although I have walked many clients through the frustration that something they built could not be saved between sessions, I have had experiences of seeing the therapeutic relationship strengthened when the client knows that their build will be waiting for them at the next session.

Mazes

Suggested Age Group: 3 and up

Therapeutic Benefits: Problem solving, executive functioning, frustration tolerance, asking for help

Telehealth Benefits: Mazes are a simple activity that can challenge a client while engaging them in a fun way. When the client marks up the maze on their screen, they can easily erase mistakes and try again. In addition, online maze generators allow for infinite possibilities, and you never run out of novel mazes for the client to solve. You can tailor the maze's difficulty based on the client's developmental level and preferred amount of challenge. With so many options for the mazes you can generate, this activity remains new and challenging to clients over time.

Setup: There are many websites that generate mazes that you can use in your sessions; I typically use http://www.mazegenerator.net/. Go to the site and input your preferred settings—these include the shape (rectangle, circle, triangle, or hexagon), width, height, inner width, inner height, and starting point. You can also choose different cell shapes depending on the overall maze shape. After you have selected your settings, click "generate." You can then download the generated maze and share it with the client using screen share.

Minecraft

Suggested Age Group: 10 and up

Therapeutic Benefits: Teamwork, creativity, exploration of emotions

Telehealth Benefits: Minecraft is a popular computer game, and it seems to have staying power: Children have been excitedly telling me about their Minecraft worlds for 10 years. In this game, kids create elaborate, intricate worlds tailored to their aesthetic preferences and desires, and they have the option to go into survival mode, where they defend their creations from aggressors. These options mean that kids can show you what their play needs are and have those needs addressed in the way that works best for them.

While kids would often tell me about Minecraft in our in-person sessions, I did not permit them to play Minecraft during our appointments until I transitioned to telehealth. If a child has a Minecraft account, they can bring me into the game with them using screen share. If they have an interest in the game but do not own it, there is a free multiplayer version that you can use.

Setup (Free Version): The version of Minecraft that I use in sessions is available here: https://www.crazygames.com/game/minecraft-classic. Select "play now," and you will be shown a link that you can share with up to nine clients, so this activity works for individual sessions or groups. Choose a nickname, send the link to your client, and click "start."

When you and the client are both in the game, you can follow the client's lead to build anything you and your client can imagine.

Setup (Paid Version): If a client already owns Minecraft, you could allow them to use their paid version during your sessions. They can log in to their appointment from the device that they use to play Minecraft and share their screen with you. From there, they can show you what they have created in their world. When a client shows me their version of Minecraft, I have them explore with me the world they created and discuss what this world means for them. Is this a safe place where they feel in control? Is it a place where they have the power to fight off bad guys? Did they focus on making a beautiful landscape or the perfect home? Since worldbuilding can be time-consuming, having the client show me what they created prior to the session lets us open with this exploration.

Physical Play

Suggested Age Group: 3 and up

Therapeutic Benefits: Nondirective play, exploration of emotions, communication skills

Telehealth Benefits: Physical play (or play therapy using physical toys) presents unique challenges in a telehealth setting. You are limited to the selection of toys the client has on hand, and you cannot engage directly with the child in a physical way. For example, if a child needs help manipulating something on the toy, you cannot reach over and assist them.

Although this means that physical play looks different in telehealth than in in-person sessions, this does not mean that it is impossible or that there are not benefits to this intervention. For instance, although you cannot provide specific toys, children sometimes delve more into play with their own toys, which are familiar to them and belong to them. In addition, you can encourage them to work through frustration, since you are not able to physically intervene.

Setup: In a psychoanalytic approach to play therapy, the therapist typically does not engage directly in play with the child; rather, the therapist observes and narrates as the child plays. This translates easily to a telehealth session if the child brings their physical toys to their appointment. However, you can still engage in interactive play in a telehealth session by bringing your own physical toys.

Set up your home office so that your toys are visible in the video frame. A small box or laptop stand will allow you to set toys down but keep them in the child's view. Engage in play as you would in your in-person sessions, having the client to prompt you verbally with how they want you to manipulate your toys.

Physical play feels awkward at first in a telehealth session, but it becomes much more natural as you practice.

Additional Resource: I recommend checking out Dr. KatySue Tillman's videos on YouTube. She shares some excellent demonstrations for physical play over telehealth, as well as free webinars for tele-play therapy.

Puppet Show

Suggested Age Group: 3 and up

Therapeutic Benefits: Exploration of emotions, exploration of relationships, communication skills, social skills

Telehealth Benefits: Puppets provide kids with an outlet for emotions in an indirect way, which can feel safer to them. They can explore different situations and feelings from the puppet's perspective rather than owning those things personally. This can help lower inhibitions and guardedness in the session.

The virtual puppet show allows the client to manipulate the size of various puppets, giving them more control over the environment and giving you more information about their experience of the activity. They can choose from different backdrops, like a school or the beach. And, as with all tele-play activities, you do not have to think about cleaning up or sanitizing puppets between sessions.

Setup: Go to https://onlinepuppets.org/, share your screen, and grant remote control to the client. There are several different puppets that the client can use, and there are animation options to have the puppets hug, jump, speak, or hit each other. Since it is difficult for both of you to manipulate puppets on the screen simultaneously, you may want to have a physical puppet on hand to interact with the client's puppets on the screen.

This is an excellent nondirective activity that is easy to incorporate in telehealth sessions, especially with very young clients.

Roblox: Adopt Me

Suggested Age Group: 7 and up

Therapeutic Benefits: Exploration of emotions, exploration of relationships, attachment

Telehealth Benefits: According to Roblox's statistics, Adopt Me is the most popular platform in the Roblox world. In this activity, clients can choose to find a pet that needs a home and take it in, and there are many different pets that they can collect. Pets can be traded with other players, or players can keep and care for the pets themselves. This lends itself to discussion of attachments, and this activity has been especially popular among kids who are adopted or who have been in foster care.

Although Roblox's platform allows chat and interaction between players, Adopt Me has the option to use a private server, and even the public server has limitations on the chat feature to ensure privacy and prevent inappropriate content from being shared.

Setup: In order to play Roblox, you have to create a free account and download the game onto your hard drive. To play Adopt Me in a telehealth session, you can have the client share their screen, or you can join their server with your own account. By joining their server, you can be more active in the game, and your avatars can interact with each other, but in my own experience, it is easier to follow what the client is doing if they are sharing their screen with me.

The client can go through the adoption process, and you can narrate, question, and work through relational concerns and attachment issues using this game.

Roblox: Hide-and-Seek

Suggested Age Group: 7 and up

Therapeutic Benefits: Planning, problem solving, exploration of emotions, exploration of relationships, communication skills

Telehealth Benefits: Roblox's platform has dozens of hide-and-seek games that you and your client can play together. This is closer to the feel of in-person sessions than the hide-and-seek game involving Google Street View, as each of you plays a character, and you hide from each other in a virtual space. This space has more hiding options than you would have in your office. It's similar to playing in real life, but you and the client can talk through the experience of the game through the telehealth platform as you are playing.

Setup: In order to play this game together, you and your client need to both create free Roblox accounts and download the game onto your telehealth devices. Then you or your client can create a private server in the game and invite the other. Your client can choose from the many hide-and-seek games on the website based on themes that interest them.

Once you enter the server, the game automatically assigns who is "it," and the other player must find a hiding place.

Roblox: Meep City

Suggested Age Group: 7 and up

Therapeutic Benefits: Exploration of emotions, exploration of relationships, mindfulness and relaxation, visualization

Telehealth Benefits: In Meep City, residents get to create their own living space, which can be an apartment, a house, or any other home that they desire. Although templates are available, players have the freedom to customize every single detail in their space. They can create a safe space for themselves with whatever colors, designs, and items that they want in their space.

Since this customization can be time-consuming, I usually have clients bring a space that they have already created into the session rather than using sessions to create the space. I can then bring the client's awareness to the experience of being in this space and how they benefit from having a place of their own.

The homes that players create have options for things like sitting by the fireplace, sleeping in a comfortable bed, or making hot chocolate. Although the virtual setting does not allow the client to have the actual physical experience of tasting the hot chocolate on their tongue or feeling the warmth of the fire on their skin, they can visualize these things as their avatar experiences them.

Setup: You can create a Roblox account and have your avatar join your client on a private server to tour their house, but I have found it is easier to navigate the space if the client simply shares their screen with me. I ask them to give me a virtual tour of their home and work on creating a visualization in their mind of the comfort they experience in the virtual living space that they can mentally return to any time they need to feel safe or calm.

Tag

Suggested Age Group: 6 and up

Therapeutic Benefits: Impulse control, frustration tolerance, focus

Telehealth Benefits: Kids like to play tag. It is fun, builds connection, and gets them moving, but in my office, there is not enough room to run around. Over telehealth, you can play virtual tag—you do not get the movement benefits, since your characters are on a screen, but the strategy and focus components are the same.

Setup: Go to https://www.crazygames.com/game/2-player-tag, share your screen, and grant the client remote control. You will be able to simultaneously control your pieces using keyboards when the client accepts screen control (this game requires that you and the client both be on computers with physical keyboards to play). Decide who will be red and who will be blue; the red player uses W, A, S, and D to move, and blue uses the up, down, left, and right arrows. Press left, right, A, and D at the same time to start the game. The two squares will appear on a platform, and the computer randomizes who starts off as "it." Chase each other around the platform, trying to tag each other, just as in a real-life game of tag.

This variation on the game has a time limit; whoever is "it" when the time runs out loses, and the other player gets a point. You can play several rounds and see who gains the most points. The timer feature makes transitions easier at the end of the session, as you can cue the child that "this is our last round for today."

Virtual Backgrounds

Suggested Age Group: 3 and up

Therapeutic Benefits: Imagination, creativity, nondirective play, communication skills

Telehealth Benefits: Imaginative play is an important component of play therapy. Kids need the space to explore creatively in order to develop and process emotions in a way that is age appropriate. One way to bring imaginative play into a telehealth session is to use virtual backgrounds. If you can find an image of something, it can become the backdrop to your session. Sometimes, simply pulling up an interesting background can help a child engage in the telehealth session if they are feeling distracted. You can also demonstrate that you are listening to your client's preferences by switching to backgrounds at their command to match their play.

Setup: It can be helpful to have several virtual backgrounds that you can easily switch to. Here are some types of backgrounds that I often use:

Natural:

- Underwater in the ocean
- In a forest during the day
- In a scary forest at night
- In a cave
- On a mountain
- Flying through the sky
- On a beach
- In a winter wonderland
- At the Grand Canyon

Industrial:

- In an office in a city
- In front of a city skyline
- In a library
- In a nice apartment
- In a prison cell

Vehicles:

- In the driver's seat of a car
- In the back of a police car
- Piloting a fighter jet
- Riding a bus

Outer Space:

- On board the Enterprise
- On the Moon
- On the International Space Station
- In space

Child's Interests:

- In a meme
- Godzilla
- Dinosaurs
- Minecraft world
- Roblox world
- Cartoon backgrounds (*SpongeBob SquarePants, Adventure Time,* etc.)
- Disney World
- *Lord of the Rings*
- Unicorns

Children might want a background that you do not have handy. This is easy to rectify; simply share your screen, go to Google Images, search the client's interest, and let them choose which background they would like to see. Save the preferred image and upload it to your platform's virtual backgrounds.

Children might have you navigate between backgrounds as you play; for example, a child had me drive a car and then stated that they were a police officer who pulled me over for speeding. The child told me that I was under arrest, so I toggled from the driver's seat background to the police car background. The client then instructed me to go to jail, so I made the jail cell my background. This is similar to when clients in my office use the toy handcuffs to pretend to arrest me for breaking a law in our game.

Virtual backgrounds bring imaginative play to a more realistic level in your telehealth sessions, and they let your client control their therapy space similarly to how they could manipulate physical toys in your office.

Most manualized treatment interventions can be adapted to telehealth quite easily, as you can use the screen share and annotate features to share and fill out worksheets and other activities on the screen just like you would with physical paper in a session. I have found it helpful to create digital versions of worksheets that I use a lot because I can easily adapt the sheet to the client's specific needs. For example, if a child has a particular trigger that is mentioned in the worksheet, I can change that bit and better meet their unique needs.

When completing cognitive behavioral therapy (CBT) activities over telehealth, you can save completed sheets by taking a screenshot. You can also email any activities to be practiced in between sessions. I suggest making any PDF documents fillable, as not everyone has access to a printer, and this can make worksheets more accessible to clients who prefer to fill them out online.

This section includes eight kid-friendly CBT activities designed for implementation over telehealth. These activities are common CBT interventions that might be used in person, with specific tips tailored to the telehealth platform.

The next page contains a Feelings Thermometer, which can be used with any activity in this book but is specifically prompted in the CBT activities that follow. You can share the image of the thermometer with your client and have them identify the name of the feeling they are presently experiencing along with its intensity on a scale of 1 to 10 (with 1 being "not at all" and 10 being "the biggest I have ever had this feeling"). They can tell you verbally or use the annotate feature to draw the intensity of their feelings on the thermometer.

If a child indicates they have more than one feeling, you can tell them that this is common and okay—they can easily do the feelings thermometer activity for each feeling they are currently experiencing.

Feelings Thermometer

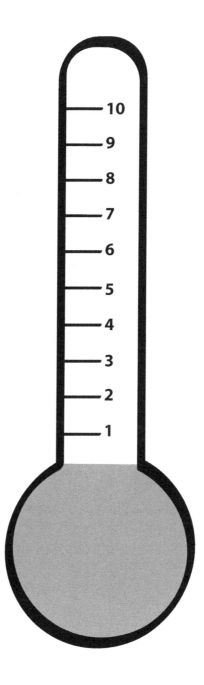

Feeling: _____

Big Breath Activities

Suggested Age Group: 3 and up

Therapeutic Benefits: Mindfulness and relaxation, coping skills, exploration of emotions, emotion regulation

Telehealth Benefits: Breathing activities are a quick and easy way to help clients regulate and center themselves. If a child is feeling hyperactive and needs to settle into the session, you can prompt them (gently, not punitively) to take some breaths with you to keep themselves engaged in the session and centered in the frame.

Below is a sample script for a big breathing activity. You can substitute your favorite breathing activity or find one online. Prompt the client to name their feeling and rank it on the 1-to-10 scale before and after doing this activity. This way, they will notice exactly how the activity affects how they feel in their body.

Prompt: "I think it would help us right now if we took some big breaths! We are breathing all the time, but we don't always stop to think about it or notice what breathing feels like to our bodies. Sometimes, when I have a big feeling, it helps to just take a moment to focus on my breathing.

"Take a second to find a comfortable position, relaxed but not slouched over. Close your eyes if you feel comfortable, and start to notice your breath. Where do you notice your breathing? In your stomach? Chest? Nose? There is no right or wrong answer; just notice whatever you feel.

"Now put one hand on your stomach. When you breathe in next, I want you to see how big you can make your stomach with the breath. See if you can make your stomach huge like Santa Claus as you breathe in through your nose as I count, 1... 2... 3... 4... 5, and when you think your lungs are completely filled with air, see if you can inhale just a tiny bit more.

"Hold your breath, 1... 2... 3.

"Now softly blow all that air out through your mouth, pushing it all the way out, like you're blowing bubbles, 1... 2... 3... 4... 5... 6... 7.

"Let's breathe in again, 1... 2... 3... 4... 5; hold, 1... 2... 3; and breathe out, 1... 2... 3... 4... 5... 6... 7.

"And one more time: breathe in, 1… 2… 3… 4… 5; hold, 1… 2… 3; and breathe out, 1… 2… 3… 4… 5… 6… 7.

"Now open your eyes, stretch your arms way above your head, and relax. How do you feel?"

Coping Skills Toolbox

Suggested Age Group: 6 and up

Therapeutic Benefits: Exploration of emotions, exploration of coping skills, self-regulation

Telehealth Benefits: It is especially important to work with kids on self-regulation in telehealth sessions, since you cannot follow the child if they move away from the camera or leave the room. You also cannot physically assist the child if they need prompting to use a skill or stay engaged in the session. Having the client put together a coping skills toolbox empowers them to self-regulate and can allow you to prompt a skill more easily if they are having trouble in a session.

Setup: You can use the website Canva to put this together or have the child create a toolbox in a text-based document. Focusing on one emotion at a time, ask the child how they bring down big feelings that make it difficult for them to make good choices, like mad, sad, nervous, and hyper. Encourage the child to think of other feelings that sometimes get too big for them to manage.

Have the child identify what things bring down each emotion, and encourage them to identify things that they can do independently along with things that involve asking for help from trusted adults. If a coping skill involves a physical item or location, this is fine to include, and you might encourage them to practice visualizing the item whenever it is not physically available.

Try to have the child identify three or four coping skills for each emotion, and remind them that needing these skills is not a bad thing. Identify one-word cues for each skill so the caregiver can let the child know when they notice the child is starting to have a hard time, and ensure that both the caregiver and child understand that these cues are gentle reminders, not punishments.

Have the child keep a copy of their coping skills toolbox so they can reference it any time they need to.

Reaction Videos and Emotion Identification

Suggested Age Group: 8 and up

Therapeutic Benefits: Emotion identification, exploration of emotions, social skills, communication skills

Telehealth Benefits: Other than certain guided meditations, I did not use a lot of videos in my in-person sessions because I did not want the child getting caught up in screen time rather than therapy. With telehealth, the session itself is screen time! This intervention is actually something that a child suggested when I was first doing telehealth with kids and was not sure what interventions were most appropriate. I chose to take an approach of curiosity, and when a child asked if they could show me their favorite reaction video as part of their session, I said yes.

A reaction video is meta—it is a video of someone watching another video and reacting to it. YouTubers record themselves watching other videos, and lots of kids love watching their reactions. Choosing a video of someone the child admires engages them in the session, and you can use this activity to practice identifying feelings.

Setup: Ask the child who their favorite YouTubers are. You can easily search that person's handle with "reaction video" and see what is available. Share your screen (and sound), and watch the reaction video together, noticing specifically what emotional reactions the YouTuber is having. Ask the client how they feel watching the video and how their emotional reaction to the original video is similar to or different than the YouTuber's response.

Receiving Help

Suggested Age Group: 3 and up

Therapeutic Benefits: Exploration of emotions, exploration of coping skills, relationship development, emotion regulation, communication skills

Telehealth Benefits: Everyone needs help sometimes! In my in-person sessions, clients often ask me for help if they are having trouble with a toy or puzzle, or if they start experiencing a big feeling and are having trouble de-escalating. In telehealth sessions, I cannot physically help my clients if they are having trouble with something, so teaching them to ask for and receive help appropriately can allow them to seek help from their caregivers if they are having trouble in their session. The telehealth setting forces the caregiver and child to work on this together rather than turning to the therapist to de-escalate the situation.

Setup: For this intervention, I have both the caregiver and the child present. I tell them that I want to work on asking for and receiving help, and I facilitate discussion between them about times when the child needs help regulating their emotions, how the caregiver can tell that the child is having a hard time, and the difference between emotions and behaviors (for example, many kids believe they get into trouble for feeling angry when, in fact, the trouble comes from behaviors they choose while angry).

I ask the child to choose a prompt that the caregiver can say when the child is having trouble. I explain to the caregiver that the prompt should be given in a neutral tone and in a gentle, nonpunishing way. I explain to the child that the prompt does not mean that they are in trouble, but that the caregiver has noticed that they are having a hard time. We discuss choices the child can make when they hear the prompt (taking some space, using a coping skill, etc.). Ask the caregiver and child to practice using the prompt between sessions as a way for the child to receive help without letting their feelings cause a behavior that gets them into trouble.

Safety Planning

Suggested Age Group: 3 and up

Therapeutic Benefits: Exploration of emotions, exploration of coping skills, communication skills, safety

Telehealth Benefits: You should have general safety plans in place for all clients when you practice therapy, with variances based on individual client needs. A client who is referred due to test anxiety with no history of safety concerns is different than a client who is referred following a psychiatric hospitalization for suicide behavior, for example.

Safety planning is one thing that becomes more complicated with telehealth. If you see clients who are not in your immediate geographic area, you will need to know what resources they have available to them. This intervention will help you put together appropriate safety protocols for each client.

A safety plan is *not* a safety contract. A safety contract is a document that the client signs committing that they will not engage in self-harm or suicide behavior between sessions, and these have not been shown to reduce harm. A safety plan, instead, is a document detailing what steps will be taken if the client is in crisis; these have been shown to be much more effective.

Setup: The following is a safety plan worksheet for use with clients. It can be adapted for level of risk and individual client needs, and it can be filled out in session via screen share. This is something I bring up early in treatment to ensure that a plan is in place if a crisis arises between sessions. It is important that both the client and their caregiver are on the same page about the safety plan, so I bring both into the session.

The Coping Skills Toolbox and Receiving Help activities presented earlier in this chapter can help you complete the safety plan.

Safety Plan

Name: _____

Address: _____

When do I have trouble being safe? _____

_____

_____

What do I do that is unsafe? _____

_____

_____

What coping skills can I use to stay safe? _____

_____

_____

What can my parent or guardian do to help me be safe? ___

_____

_____

If it's not safe for me to be at home, we will call: _____

_____

_____

If it's not safe for me to be at home, we will go to: _____

_____

_____

Thought Record

Suggested Age Group: 8 and up

Therapeutic Benefits: Cognitive restructuring, reframing, cognitive challenging, metacognition

Telehealth Benefits: Telehealth platforms make it easy to present a thought record and tailor it to the client's individual needs. You can change any component of the thought record if it does not fit your client.

Setup: I start by explaining what a thought record is in a way that fits the client's developmental level. Usually I let them know that most people have thoughts they do not agree with or find distressing, and we can learn to change those thoughts by paying attention to them. If you are well-versed in CBT, you already have a preferred introduction to thought records that you can use here—the explanation of what a thought record is stays the same over telehealth.

Since telehealth makes customization so easy, instead of showing the client a premade thought record, I use a spreadsheet to put together a thought record based on the client's individual needs. The main components of the thought record (Situation, Mood with Scale, and Thoughts) should be included, but the client can decide what the scale looks like, how thoughts should be organized, whether they want to assess mood or situation first, and so on.

By letting the client create their own thought record, they gain a sense of control over the activity and are more likely to engage.

Thought-Stopping Activity:
SKIP THE SONG

Suggested Age Group: 3 and up

Therapeutic Benefits: Cognitive refocusing, cognitive challenging, coping skills

Telehealth Benefits: Using devices in sessions makes it easy to incorporate music and videos when appropriate. This is a variation on a thought-stopping activity that I have done with clients in person where they would imagine a song they dislike coming on the radio and change the station. In telehealth, they get to take this activity more literally. You can use any platform for playing music; one that the child is familiar with will work best.

Prompt: "Sometimes we have thoughts that we don't like or that we disagree with. It can be hard to remember that we don't always choose our thoughts and that we can choose to turn a thought off if it's unpleasant.

"Think about a thought you've had that was upsetting or felt bad to you. It can be any thought you don't like. I want you to also think of something that makes you feel very happy and calm. Maybe a memory of a time that was really good for you, or a place where you feel really safe.

"Now think of two songs: one that you love and one that you can't sand. Imagine that the happy thought is the good song, and the hurtful thought is the bad song. I'm going to play the song you don't like. I want you to change over to the good song. [*Give the client remote control of your screen so that they can change the song.*]

"You can change your thoughts just like you changed the song! It takes a lot of practice, but when you notice the bad thought come on, you can switch over to the thought you like."

Tornado Brain

Suggested Age Group: 6 and up

Therapeutic Benefits: Cognitive challenging, cognitive restructuring, coping skills, visualization

Telehealth Benefits: The tornado simulator gives an excellent visualization of how it feels to be in a negative thought spiral. Kids can see how they are impacted when their big thoughts get out of control, and it promotes discussion about how to slow their thoughts down.

Setup: Go to https://scijinks.gov/tornado-simulation/ and share your screen. You will see the simulator when the page loads. For the first demonstration, use the dials on top of the simulator to make the tornado as big as possible with the highest speed possible. Ask the client to think of their negative thoughts as a big, fast tornado that takes down houses and trees. Have them explore the progression of their thoughts, how one thought led to another.

Next, reset the simulator and turn the size of the tornado all the way down, and put the speed at the lowest setting. When you start, you will see that the tornado is still there, but when it passes over the house and trees, they are not damaged.

Prompt: "We can't always make the tornado go away—sometimes those thoughts pop up without warning and want to stick around. But you can use your skills to slow the tornado down so it does not damage things as it passes through."

Questions:

1. What kinds of things put a tornado in your brain?

2. What things slow down your tornado?

3. It can be hard to shrink a tornado once it gets really big. How do you notice when the wind is picking up but maybe a whole tornado hasn't formed yet?

The activities presented in this toolbox should set you up to practice telehealth with a wide range of clients with different presenting problems. But what if there is a particular game or intervention that you love using for in-person sessions but is not listed here?

Just like in your in-person office, telehealth with kids is about being flexible and creative. A good starting point is to list the interventions you have used in person and think about what each of these could look like in a telehealth session. Thanks to the screen share feature, you can easily incorporate any worksheet into a telehealth session, and digitized versions of worksheets are easy to customize to your client's unique needs, preferences, and treatment goals. For example, if a client is triggered by a specific word, you can easily remove that word from the worksheet.

As for games and other activities, you can often find a virtual version of the same item you use in person, or you can create your own online activities and customize them however you like. Many games already exist online and can be brought into telehealth sessions either by sharing a private link or by sharing your screen and taking turns using screen control. The following section will take you through each approach.

Finding Activities

An easy way to find telehealth activities is to search online for virtual equivalents of the games and toys you use in your in-person sessions. You can search for a particular one or browse within a website that offers a variety of activities. Each of the following sites includes a number of games that I have found to be well-suited to telehealth:

- https://www.agame.com/
- https://www.coolmathgames.com/
- https://www.crazygames.com/
- https://www.helpfulgames.com/
- https://playingcards.io/
- https://poki.com
- https://scratch.mit.edu/

YouTube is a good place to search for guided meditations, stretches, breathing exercises, and other activities for which video tutorials are helpful. The benefit of using a video is that you are doing the activity directly with the child rather than instructing them. In addition, the video might show the child a way to approach the activity that is different than what you might show them (more perspectives can be a good thing!). I have bookmarked and subscribed to a few channels that I have found helpful:

- Cosmic Kids Yoga:
  https://www.youtube.com/user/CosmicKidsYoga
- The Honest Guys:
  https://www.youtube.com/user/TheHonestGuys
- Meditation Channel:
  https://www.youtube.com/channel/UC547M_JrY273-0ZU3aMDfMA
- The Mental Health Teacher:
  https://www.youtube.com/channel/UCFmUuRhirRUPRtROX0KiQcw
- Moovlee:
  https://www.youtube.com/channel/UCsSS5kMpKCaJ_HhTM9-HKHg
- New Horizon—Meditation & Sleep Stories:
  https://www.youtube.com/channel/UCjW-3doUmNsyY5aLQHLiNXg
- Smile and Learn—English:
  https://www.youtube.com/channel/UCxoDMG0tvaYO5Xobvtqw5nw

I also recommend inviting your clients to suggest activities they enjoy doing at home—online games they already play, toys or art supplies they have on hand, and so on. Some of my clients have suggested activities that I would not have thought of otherwise or that would not have been possible to do in my in-person office, and kids enjoy sharing their favorite activities with you. Not only that, but kids tend to be more engaged if they feel that you are truly listening to their input, and they will be more invested in an activity that they helped create.

Creating Your Own Activities

When I can't find an online version of a board or card game that I want to use in a telehealth session, I use .pcio files. There are a number of websites that support these files, but I primarily use PlayingCards.IO because I find their custom rooms intuitive and easy to navigate.

Navigate to PlayingCards.IO in your web browser. Scroll down to "other/custom" and click on it, then select "start blank room," and "enter." On the left side, you will see a suitcase icon. Click on it to edit the room.

Under "click to add widgets," you can import standard card decks, custom card decks (including customized images that you can upload), domino sets, marbles, checkers, pins, poker chips, and custom pieces. You can also add automation buttons that can do things like shuffle a deck of cards or reset the game, timers, counters, and spinners. Lastly, you can add headings, text, and boards. Dozens of free and royalty-free game board images are available online, and if you are using the files solely in your own practice, you can take photographs of your own game boards and upload them to the platform. Since every component of the platform is customizable, you can even develop your own therapeutic board games to use in your practice.

In the blank room, upload all the images you need to play your game, including the board, cards, and pieces, and add all the other components you will need, like spinners (for dice), pawns, and chips. Once everything looks how you want it, toggle over to "room options." You have the option for the room to have hands for each player, which allows you to hold cards that the other players cannot see. Export your file and save it in a location where you can keep track of it—my desktop has a folder labeled "Board Games" for this purpose.

This platform can be used for activities other than games too. I created a set of feelings cards by drawing various emoji faces and uploading them into a custom deck of cards. For another file, I uploaded a body outline as the custom board with different colored chips. The client uses the chips to identify where they feel different emotions in their body and what those emotions feel like.

When you want to use .pcio files in a session, go to PlayingCards.IO, create a blank room, and click the "edit" icon. In the "room options" tab under "import/export room," select "import from file" and choose the desired file. This will bring the game into your room. Share the link with your client and have them join you in the room.

When using .pcio files, you and the client can control everything in the room simultaneously, so you both can move cards around, manipulate pieces, and engage with the game together. This allows for a nondirective approach to the game and gives play a similar feel to when you are meeting in person.

Another benefit of having several .pcio files saved on your hard drive is that they simplify transitions during the session. Some kids (especially younger kids) might have difficulty navigating different links; if you are using .pcio files, you can have the caregiver set up one game room and import the different files your client requests.

Playing to Your (Telehealth) Strengths

Telehealth has unique advantages compared to in-person sessions. You can leverage these strengths when adding new activities to your telehealth toolbox and when selecting appropriate interventions to use based on each client's interests, needs, and treatment goals.

Many online games have built-in rules, so the client cannot cheat or change the rules in order to win. This presents an opportunity to work on frustration tolerance and emotion regulation without sacrificing rapport (because you are not the one making and enforcing the rules). Some games provide additional help by showing each player their possible moves (or even automatically making certain moves), keeping track of the score, or generating questions or prompts for the players to use. This reduces the amount of work you need to do to simply keep the game going, which allows more time for conversation with your client.

In addition, virtual activities often have more options for customization than you would be able to offer in person. This is especially true for art activities: Your clients can choose from a wider variety of colors that will never run out. They can even erase parts of their drawing if they choose, which helps them feel more comfortable expressing their thoughts and feelings in the drawing and gives you greater insight into their process and perspective.

One of my favorite things about telehealth is that cleanup is as simple as the click of a button. You do not have to spend time sanitizing toys, vacuuming up sand, washing paintbrushes, or searching for lost puzzle pieces. And in some cases, such as when you are using Mecabricks or Minecraft in place of physical LEGO® sets, clients can save their work for the next session.

Keeping these unique advantages of telehealth in mind will help you to develop activities that go beyond simply replicating what you would do in an in-person session. Transitioning to telehealth gives you opportunities to find and create new activities, spend less of the session time doing setup or cleanup, and customize your approach to meet each client's needs.

You've Got This!

Now you have everything you need to provide telehealth to children and adolescents. You possess the skills to build your confidence, explain telehealth to caregivers, and engage even young or hyperactive children in sessions. Not only that, but you have a robust toolbox of activities to build skills and achieve each client's unique treatment goals, as well as the knowledge to turn anything you use in person into an effective telehealth intervention. Telehealth is here to stay, and you have the resources to provide the best care possible to your clients!

References

Archard, P. J., O'Reilly, M., Fitzpatrick, S., & Fox, J. (2021). Youth telemental health and COVID-19. *Irish Journal of Psychological Medicine*, 1–2. http://doi.org/10.1017/ipm.2021.27

Cantor, J. H., McBain, R. K., Kofner, A., Stein, B. D., & Yu, H. (2021). Availability of outpatient telemental health services in the United States at the outset of the COVID-19 pandemic. *Medical Care*, *59*(4), 319–323. http://doi.org/10.1097/MLR.0000000000001512

Felker, B. L., McGinn, M. M., Shearer, E. M., Raza, G. T., Gold, S. D., Kim, J. M., Rojas, S. M., Roussev, M. S., Varkovitzky, R. L., Liu, H., Morrison, K. L., & McCann, R. A. (2021). Implementation of a telemental health training program across a mental health department. *Telemedicine Reports*, *2*(1), 26–31. http://doi.org/10.1089/tmr.2020.0011

Gloff, N. E., LeNoue, S. R., Novins, D. K., & Myers, K. (2015). Telemental health for children and adolescents. *International Review of Psychiatry*, *27*(6), 513–524. https://doi.org/10.3109/09540261.2015.1086322

Moody Fairchild, R., Ferng-Kuo, S.-F., Rahmouni, H., & Hardesty, D. (2020). Telehealth increases access to care for children dealing with suicidality, depression, and anxiety in rural emergency departments. *Telemedicine and e-Health*, *26*(11), 1353–1362. http://doi.org/10.1089/tmj.2019.0253

Schoenfelder Gonzalez, E., Myers, K., Thompson, E. E., King, D. A., Glass, A. M., & Penfold, R. B. (2021). Developing home-based telemental health services for youth: Practices from the SUAY study. *Journal of Telemedicine and Telecare*, *27*(2),110–115. http://doi.org/10.1177/1357633X19863208

Sharma, A., Sasser, T., Schoenfelder Gonzalez, E., Vander Stoep, A., & Myers, K. (2020). Implementation of home-based telemental health in a large child psychiatry department during the COVID-19 crisis. *Journal of Child and Adolescent Psychopharmacology*, *30*(7), 404–413. http://doi.org/10.1089/cap.2020.0062

Made in the USA
Coppell, TX
03 September 2023

21137859R00090